Consciousness, Matter, and Energy

Consciousness, Matter, and Energy

The Emergence of Mind in Nature

Benjamin Pinkel

Turover Press
Santa Monica, California

To Anne and Sheila

Contents

Preface

There exists in nature an invisible realm of being in which lie the "exciters" that motivate the flow of physical and mental events. The existence of this realm of being, generally overlooked by scientists, can be inferred from a consideration of the scientific literature.

In the physical world the exciters implement, for example, gravitational and electrical phenomena. They are represented in science by equations (e.g., Newton's, Maxwell's, and Schrodinger's) which can be used to specify quantitatively gravitational and electrical fields and also their effects on material things. But the mode of existence of these exciters and their means of moving material things are beyond comprehension.

The exciters are involved in all interactions between material things. A simple example of the role of the exciters is afforded by the rebounding of two billiard balls after impacting. This rebounding is not produced by the direct impact of the matter in one ball on the matter in the other ball. Instead, the rebounding is caused by the rejection of the atoms of each ball by the electric fields of the other ball, acting according to the laws of the exciter. The matter of each ball occupies only one-trillionth of the volume of the ball and its atoms are held in their array in the ball by their electric fields.

In the purely physical world the existence of an exciter is revealed by the motion of material objects, and the laws of the exciter are inferred from an analysis of this motion. For example, the existence of an exciter called gravity was inferred from the fact that the earth appeared to be attracted toward the sun, and the gravitational law was inferred by Isaac Newton from the observation that the orbit of the earth around the sun is elliptical.

Introspection reveals a special kind of exciter called the mind. It is special in that it subjectively experiences internal events such as sensations, emotions, and thoughts. Interactions between the mental and physical worlds are mediated by the brain. Some insight into these interactions can be obtained from a consideration of brain structure and processes. All information is transmitted to and through the brain as electrical impulses passing through nerve cells called neurons. Through the agency of the brain, physical events can generate mental events, and mental events can cause movements in the physical world. For example, through the agency of associated structures and neural connections with and in the brain, photons discharged by a hot metal on striking the retina of the eye can induce the mental experience of light, air vibrations entering the ear can induce the mental experience of sound, and special molecules emanating from a flower can, on striking the nose, induce the mental experience of odor. A mental event can cause a physical event. The thought that I wish to lift my right arm can be followed by the lifting of the arm. A thought can cause a subsequent thought as in an analytic process.

In physical science new energy concepts and the associated laws are introduced when new phenomena are discovered that cannot be explained in terms of the existing energies. Because the introspective awareness of mental phenomena cannot be explained in terms of the energies of physical science (e.g., gravitational, electrical, and kinetic energy), it appears reasonable to propose a new energy, namely, energy of mind (vis mentis), and its special laws. Some of these laws can be expressed in mathematical terms, like the relation between the intensity of a light beam impinging on the eye of a person and the intensity of the mental experience of light reported by that person (the Weber-Fechner law). Other laws presently can be expressed only as cause-and-effect statements as employed by psychologists and psychiatrists.

These energies and their laws in both the physical and mental domains are useful surrogates for the associated exciters because through their use scientists can predict the course of natural phenomena; they are not the exciters themselves.

The means whereby the interactions between the physical and mental domains are implemented is not understood. Information from a sensory system arrives at its final staging area in the brain where it establishes a physical structure, possibly an ionic structure to represent it. Up to this point the process is open to physical investigation. What cannot be investigated and may never be understood is the process within the exciter called the mind whereby the physical structure in the final staging area is translated into a mental experience (like a flash of light or a sound or an odor, etc.). How a thought initiated in the mind affects brain processes to assist in the development of the thought and to provide a bodily action at the will of the mind is also a profound mystery.

There are today many scientists, philosophers, and psychologists who, because they perceive no physical basis for mind nor for the interaction between mind and the physical world, reject mind as a reality in nature. They are classified as mechanists and behaviorists. A major objective of this book is to point out that the lack of understanding of the modes of existence and operation of mind as an exciter is not a valid basis for rejecting the reality of mind, otherwise one would have to reject the reality of the exciters in the theories proposed by physical scientists (e.g., gravity and electricity) on the same grounds. This book proposes an expansion of the scientific view of nature to include a concept of mind.

Our universe had its beginning approximately fifteen billion years ago when the matter of the universe was gathered into a relatively small volume, a colossal explosion, called the "big bang," occurred, and the debris of the explosion emerged at high velocity into the expanding space of the universe. Because of the extremely high temperature generated by this explosion, the matter was reduced to its fundamental particles, namely, electrons and quarks. The great complexity of the many objects and beings that one now sees in the universe suggests that the exciters that molded these entities must have been in operation since very early in cosmic time. It is, however, only recently in the history of mankind that the exciters of physical processes have been discovered by scientists. It is reasonable to believe that all the exciters in nature have not yet been discovered. This thought inspires imaginative speculation on what functions these yet undiscovered exciters might perform.

All the topics mentioned in this summary are discussed in this book in terms that are understandable to the nonscientist as well as the scientist.

Acknowledgments

I gratefully acknowledge the valuable comments of the following people who read portions of the text: Hugh R. Wilson, Professor, University of Chicago; I. Irving Pinkel, Associate Director (ret.) of the Lewis Research Center, NASA, Cleveland, Ohio; Sheila M. Pinkel, Assistant Professor of Art, Pomona College, Claremont, California.

I am also grateful to Anne A. Pinkel, formerly Technical Editor at the Langley Research Center, NACA (now NASA), who edited much of the text, and to Jack R. Miles, Book Editor of the *Los Angeles Times,* for his faith in the book and his continuing interest and support.

Whatever flaws remain in the text are my personal contributions.

Part One

The Point of View

Possibly the earliest concept of the mind-body relation on record derives from the belief that consciousness, or mind, is a manifestation of the soul, a mysterious entity that inhabits and controls the body. Socrates and Plato held this view. René Descartes, the seventeenth-century philosopher, credited with initiating the modern approach to philosophic inquiry, also subscribed to this concept. This belief is still held by many people of religious persuasion.

Chapter One

Introduction

The relation between the mind and the body has long been, and still is, a subject of much controversy. Investigation of this subject by philosophers, which in recent years involved the logic of language, produced no compelling conclusions.

The controversy turns on whether (a) mind is a myth as believed by the behaviorists, or (b) mind is a complementary aspect of the physical processes in the brain unable to influence these processes, or (c) mind is an autonomous entity in the brain, called pejoratively by philosopher Gilbert Ryle "the ghost in the machine," which can exert control over some brain processes and thereby impose its will on the performance of the body.

In the twentieth century neurologists have provided a considerable amount of information on brain structure and processes. And physicists have revised their conception of the relation of science to nature, which has a bearing on our understanding of body structure and physical interactions. The reexamination of the mind-body problem in the light of this new scientific information is the objective of this book.

Possibly the earliest concept of the mind-body relation on record derives from the belief that consciousness, or mind, is a manifestation of the soul, a mysterious entity that inhabits and controls the body. Socrates and Plato held this view. René Descartes, the seventeenth-century philosopher, credited with initiating the modern approach to philosophic inquiry, also subscribed to this concept. This belief is still held by many people of religious persuasion.

3

With the development of the physical sciences, other concepts of the mind-body relation came into being. Up to roughly the end of the nineteenth century the great advances in the understanding of the physical laws of nature inspired the proposition that the entire cosmos, including all the living things in it, is a great system of matter and energy that moves and changes in response to mechanistic laws. In consonance with this proposition, John Watson, the father of the behavioristic school of psychology in the early part of the twentieth century, held that man is a stimulus-response machine and that consciousness and mind are myths, merely names applied to certain classes of behavior. Epiphenomenalists, like T. H. Huxley, also accept the mechanistic view of man but they believe in the reality of the phenomenon of consciousness. They cast consciousness in the role of an impotent bystander, registering the implications of the physical processes in the body but unable to interfere with these processes. Both mechanistic views have currently many adherents in scientific and philosophical circles.

Although the epiphenomenalist is willing to accept the existence of mental events on the basis of his personal subjective experiences, he cannot understand how this nonmaterial entity could possibly affect the physical processes in the brain to thereby influence the person's behavior. Whether or not interaction between the mind and the brain is a possibility is at the heart of the mind-brain problem. I will endeavor to show that modern physical science does, however, allow for the effect of nonmaterial entities on the behavior of physical objects, and that the emotion of understanding of even the simplest of interactions in the domain of physical science rests on a verbal foundation that collapses when probed.

There once lived a tribe of people of philosophical inclination. They felt that they understood, because it appeared to be obvious, why an unsupported object would fall down to the earth. But why did not the earth fall down? The earth, they reasoned, is supported on the back of a giant turtle. Why did not the turtle fall down? Because it rests on the back of an even larger turtle; there was no limit to the number of turtles they could posit in support of their theory. But the turtles are invisible; what proof do they have of their existence? And their answer was "obviously, if the turtles did not exist the earth would fall down."

Currently, most people, who have learned about Newton's theory of gravitation, understand that an unsupported rock is impelled to fall to the earth, and the earth is held in its orbit around the sun by the force of gravity that exists between these objects. But the force of gravity is an invisible non-material essence. How does one know that it exists? The answer, reminiscent of the kind of rationale used to support the "turtle" theory, is: If the force of gravity did not exist the rock would not fall to the ground, and the earth would not remain in its orbit around the sun.

Newton's theory in conjunction with his theory of mechanics was the dominant theory of nature for three centuries, from the time of Newton (1642–1727) until the beginning of the twentieth century. It is a better theory than the "turtle" theory because it handles a much greater range of phenomena. By using Newton's equations one can, for example, predict the position of the earth as it changes with time in its orbit around the sun. But Newton did not claim that he understood how nature implements this movement of the earth, or the movement of any other object attributed to gravity. In a letter to Richard Bentley, who lectured on Newton's theory, Newton wrote:

> You sometimes speak of gravity as essential and inherent to matter. Pray, do not ascribe that notion to me; for the cause of gravity is what I do not pretend to know.[1]

Early in the twentieth century Newtonian physics was displaced by Einstein's theory of General Relativity because the latter covers an even greater range of natural phenomena. The general theory of relativity does not involve the force of gravity; instead it postulates that the space-time continuum is curved in the vicinity of mass, and that objects are constrained to follow their world lines in this continuum. The locus of the world line for each object may be computed from Einstein's equation. But the world lines are invisible nonmaterial essences. How do we know they exist? Because if they did not exist the objects of the universe would not know where to go.

Einstein does not attempt to describe how nature mediated the movement of objects along their world lines. Nor does he claim that his theory is the final word regarding natural phenomena. In a letter to Norman Cousins, Einstein wrote:

> My ideas caused people to reexamine Newtonian physics. It is inevitable that my own ideas will be reexamined and supplanted. If they are not, there will have been a gross failure somewhere.[2]

The implication of this discussion of scientific theories is as follows. When a scientist is confronted with a set of empirical observations on the behavior of objects, he invents an invisible nonmaterial exciter (designated by the acronym NOME) that can control the behavior of objects in accordance with certain rules which he generally states in the form of mathematical equations. His theory is considered to be satisfactory if it can accurately predict the course of all phenomena to which it is expected to relate.

We may say that we understand the behavior of an object if it is in accordance with a theory that we have accepted as true, even though we do not understand the mode of existence of the NOME that mediates this behavior nor how this essence manages to interact with the object.

The scientist is made aware of objects and their behavior by sensory inputs to his mind such as pictures, sounds, and so forth. These mental events (after he has eliminated dream contributions) provide the empirical data on which he bases his theories concerning the physical world. Although the scientist is also aware of his emotions and thoughts and notes that they can affect his behavior, he opts to ignore these data because he does not understand how a mental event, a NOME, can affect a physical object.

Lack of understanding of how NOMES (like those that mediate gravitational and electrical effects) influence the behavior of objects does not prevent physicists from developing a science regarding this behavior. And I hold that this lack of understanding should not deter the search for a more complete science of nature which involves consideration of all data that engages the mind.

The previous discussion indicates that scientists view nature as, in effect, consisting of two modes of being. In one mode lie the material objects of nature, while in the other mode lie the nonmaterial essences that affect the movements of these objects. The existence of these nonmaterial essences is inferred solely from the behavior of the material objects. I place consciousness as an essence in the nonmaterial mode. Its mode of existence and its means of interacting with the brain are mysteries. In short, the destinies of all material things, the inanimate and the animate, depend on interactions with a hidden and mysterious nonmaterial world.

The discussion of the mind-body problem in this book reflects the perspective projected by the ideas presented in this chapter. Although the concept of mind as a manifestation of a supernatural entity, the soul, is briefly discussed, the book deals mainly with naturalistic concepts of mind. And it focuses on the question: Is mind an impotent by-product of the processes in the brain, unable to influence these processes (designated the mechanistic theory), or does the mind, after being created naturalistically, possess an autonomous capability, namely, the capability to exert its will on the body by influencing brain processes (designated the vis mentis theory)?

In discussing the autonomous mind theory, I have followed the lead of the physical scientists in their handling of the nonmaterial motivating essences in nature. I have attempted to provide an operationally useful theory of consciousness in terms of an energy, vis mentis, and its laws.

In Part I, I take up a number of topics that set the stage for the remainder of the book. I discuss consciousness, reality, and the reality of the Self and of the objective world. I state the primary assumption of this book, which I call the "Anatomical Premise," namely, that the human structure and its physical processes are essentially as depicted by the physiologists and neuroscientists.

I point out that the physical scientists employ mainly inductive logic rather than deductive logic in the process of conceiving a new theory from a set of empirical data. The dictionary defines induction as it relates to logic as "any form of reasoning in which the conclusion though supported by the premises does not follow from them necessarily." Inductive logic is the kind of logic a jury uses when it attempts to judge the innocence or guilt of a defendant on the basis of purely circumstantial evidence. The noted physicist Max Born (Nobel Prize 1954) said: "There is no logical path from fact to theory. Power of imagination, intuition, . . . are the sources of creative achievement." This form of logic also applies when one attempts to derive a theory about consciousness from subjective data.

The human structure and its physical processes are part of the matter-energy system of nature. I explore, in Part II, what science projects concerning matter, energy, and their laws of interaction. The primary parameter of matter is mass; only if a particle possesses mass is it matter. But mass according to physical science is a number specified by a mathematical equation. Energy likewise is a number specified by a mathematical equation. But these equations do not predict how matter and energy interact. The interactions between matter and energy are indicated by additional equations. These several sets of equations are the scientists' scheme for dealing with physical phenomena; they are not the NOME that implements the processes represented by these equations. The material substance of the body occupies only one-trillionth of the volume of the body. The atoms of the body are held in their highly distributed configuration by the electrical NOME, which might be viewed as occupying the bulk of the space in the body. And this NOME mediates most of the physical processes of the body.

An investigation of the brain-mind relationship calls for some insight into the mechanics of the brain. I describe briefly, in Part III, those aspects of the structure and processes of the brain and several of the sensory systems that feed information into the brain, which I deem useful for providing this insight.

The primary element of the brain and the nervous systems that connect with the brain is the neuron. The neuron is, in effect, a transmission line. It receives information from other neurons at its input end and supplies information to still other neurons at its output end. The brain contains on the order of 100 billion neurons and each neuron may interact with as many as 1,000 other neurons. Information passes through a neuron from its input end to its output end as slugs of mainly ionic sodium. Each ionic impulse is essentially like every other and a single impulse conveys no information. Information is conveyed by sequences of impulses and spaces between sequences. Neuroscientist Sir John Eccles (Nobel Prize 1963) draws an anology between neuronal transmission and that of a telegraph line employing a Morse code with dots only. In this manner information is transmitted not only to and from the brain but also through the processes of the brain.

The transduction of the information transmitted to the brain into mental experiences depends not only on the impulse sequences but also on where in the brain these impulses are received and processed. A description of some of the primary cerebral cortices involved in this operation is presented. I also describe the visual and auditory receptor systems that receive information from the physical world and transmit it to the brain. There is no need to go into the details of these systems here.

With regard to the visual system, the following comments may be of interest. When photons, that represent light in the physicist's description of nature, strike neurons on the retina of the eye, they ionize certain chemicals in these neurons, thereby initiating a flow of ionic impulses through the neural pathways to the visual cortex of the brain. These ionic impulses in the visual cortex, in some mysterious way, cause the mental experience of light. There is no light, as humans perceive light, shining in either the brain or the objective world.

Similarly, noise and odor are purely mental experiences; their counterparts in the physical world are air vibrations and special molecules emanating from such things as flowers. In other words, the universe was a dark, quiet, odorless place until living creatures arrived on the scene capable of mental experiences.

In Part IV, I discuss several topics relating to the brain-mind question. Is free-will a reality? Where in the brain is consciousness located? And finally I present some brain-mind concepts advanced by neuroscientists.

From an introspective review of my mental dynamics in the process of making a difficult decision, in which I note no mechanistic compulsion from either heredity or environment, but instead the angst of indecision as I attempt to make the wisest choice, I have judged that I possess free-will.

Neuroscientists do not agree on a common view of the brain-mind relationship but hold views that cover the range of philosophic concepts. Robert W. Thatcher and E. Roy John subscribe to the epiphenomenalistic view by holding that mind is a complementary aspect of certain processes in the brain; it registers the implications of these processes as mental events, but is unable to influence these processes. However, Wilder Penfield holds a free mind view in which the energy of mind is generated by naturalistic processes in the brain, but once created, exerts its will using the brain as its messenger. Eccles endorses the classical dualistic view in which mind is a manifestation of the soul, a supernatural entity instilled into each person's body by God. Karl Pribram subscribes to the view advanced by physicist David Bohm, that all minds and all substance are conjoined in a timeless, spaceless oneness in a higher realm of being, and that the here-and-now experienced by man is an illusory projection from this higher realm of being. I comment on this latter theory in this part of the book and on the two naturalistic theories in Parts V and VI.

In Part V, I deal with the concept of mind as an impotent by-product of the physical processes in the brain. I point out that the electrical field produced by the ionic movements in the brain is the most reasonable phenomenon with which to associate a mechanistic concept of mind. But can a mind conjoined point-by-point with an electric field holistically appraise the mental implications of that field or discriminate aspects of that field as discrete sensory modalities? Can this mechanistic theory of mind explain the process revealed by introspection in which the mind searches for, judges, and rejects words as it attempts to express a new and elusive thought? Can it explain the human capability for "understanding" and the infinite horizons for thought and action opened up in the areas of this understanding? After pursuing these questions at some length, I conclude that the mechanistic theory of mind is seriously deficient in its ability to account for the manner in which the human mind implements its operations.

In Part VI, I discuss a theory of consciousness in which the mind, using the brain as its messenger, can control its thought processes and can influence bodily actions. I point out that consciousness, like the motivating exciters of physical theory, cannot be described as a thing-in-itself but, like these exciters, it can be represented, for operational purposes, by an energy and its laws. I call this energy *vis mentis,* and describe some of its laws. Finally, I discuss the relation between the vis mentis theory and some concepts of the brain-mind relation advanced by philosophers.

The fact that scientists have, relatively late in the history of mankind, inferred the existence of the NOMEs represented by their equations, suggests the possibility that they have not yet discovered all the NOMEs in nature. I present in Part VII some speculations in this connection.

The NOME represented by electromagnetic waves and their associated equations for their interactions with radio equipment is a recently discovered means for the transmission of information. Reasons are given to support the speculation that there may be another NOME for more directly transmitting information at a speed not limited by the speed of light.

The genetic molecule in, for example, the embryo of a child can produce all the complex molecules needed to construct the child, can make the many components of the child in proper composition, shape, position, and interconnection to create a living organism, and can endow it with the capabilities to grow, to have mental experiences and, in time, to conceive theories concerning what it sees. This remarkable performance of the genetic molecule suggests that associated with this molecule is a NOME infinitely more capable than the NOME represented by electrical theory.

I speculate on where in the human body the field representing the NOME of consciousness might be located and the fate of this NOME on the death of the body.

There is a cosmic veil behind which exist the NOMEs that mediate the phenomena open to human perception. Humans can only guess at the nature of these NOMEs. Physical scientists conjecture from their observations on the motion of material objects, and each person from one's subjective experiences and interactions with personal bodily events. One may never directly perceive the content of the domain behind the veil nor know the full measure of that content.

Chapter Two

On the Mental and Physical Worlds and Reality

On the Genesis of Consciousness

The current prevalent scientific theory holds that our universe had its origin fifteen billion years ago. At that time the substance of the universe occupied a relatively small space, a cosmic explosion, called the "big bang," occurred, and the debris of the explosion was propelled at great velocity into the expanding space of the universe.

The temperature produced by the big bang was so great that the universe disintegrated into its elementary particles and appeared as a sea of electrons and quarks. As the universe expanded it cooled. One second after the big bang the temperature had fallen sufficiently to allow the quarks to join and form protons, the nuclei of hydrogen atoms. During the next hundred thousand years the nuclei of deuterium, helium, and lithium atoms also were formed. The universe also contained photons, namely, particles of light energy.

Active in the universe from its very beginning is a nonmaterial dynamism, currently represented in science by mathematical equations that define the forces in nature and specify their interactions with nature's particles. This dynamism, in time, molded the debris of the big bang into the objects that now constitute the universe.

But what is most remarkable about this hidden dynamism is that it eventually created *Homo sapiens,* a living species whose members are endowed with consciousness. This feat, which is beyond the range of possibilities projected by the equations of modern science, indicates that there is a major gap in the scientific representation of this dynamism.

Because consciousness does not fit into the scientific description of nature, some scientists and philosophers, who identify as behaviorists, say it is a myth. Others of religious persuasion hold that consciousness is a manifestation of the soul, which is placed into each human body by God. And still others view it as an aspect of nature that has not been addressed by science. The discussion of consciousness is the major objective of this book.

It is important at the outset of this discussion that my usage of the term *consciousness,* in contrast to some usages found in the literature, be clearly delineated.

Some Usages of the Term Consciousness

Since the time of John Locke (1632–1704) philosophers have been debating the concept of consciousness without arriving at a consensus. At issue is whether awareness of self is a necessary element in consciousness, or whether consciousness is a unified complex of various mental events even without any awareness of self, or whether even the awareness of a single sensory modality and nothing more qualifies as consciousness. This lack of consensus is reflected in the various uses of consciousness found in current literature.

The neuroscientists Thatcher and John in their book *Functional Neuroscience* define consciousness as a process in which the various sensations, perceptions, memories, needs, are combined in a unified mental experience which causes the organism to adjust to its environment.[1] There is no mention of awareness of self in this definition.

Julian Jaynes, conversely, equates consciousness with an awareness of self. In his analysis of Homer's *Iliad* he draws a distinction between our subjective conscious minds and the minds of the Myceneans. He proposes that the Myceneans possessed bicameral minds and that

> volition, planning, initiative is organized with no consciousness whatever and then "told" to the individual . . . sometimes with the visual aura of a . . . friend or . . . "god," or sometimes as a voice alone.[2]

Consciousness, Jaynes argues, came with the breakdown of the bicameral mind to achieve a unified self-aware mind.

Consciousness is employed by Jaynes and by Thatcher and John to designate a very complex, highly integrated mental state.

My Usage of Consciousness

Even the simplest case of a mental experience is a miracle from the perspective of physical science. As will be amplified later, physical science gives no hint of the possibility of mental phenomena. Nor is there a place for mental phenomena in the cosmology of physical science. I employ the word consciousness to denote any instance of this nonphysical miracle, the mental event, even though there may be no accompanying experience of self.

A bee may be motivated to fly toward a flower, when impacted by certain molecules emanating from the flower, as purely a mechanistic response. But if the bee senses the odor of the flower as a mental experience, even though it may be the only kind of mental experience it can have, the bee is experiencing the miracle of consciousness in my usage of this term.

In the human species, consciousness has evolved into the very complex manifestation described by Thatcher and John, in which many mental events, including not only several types of sensations but also emotions and thoughts, are experienced in concert.

The Self

The psychologist and philosopher William James views the concept of Self as being related to the spiritualistic concept of the soul. James describes what he believes to be the common notion of Self:

> Probably all men would describe it much the same way up to a certain point. They would call it the active element in all consciousness; saying that whatever qualities a man's feelings may possess, or whatever content his thought may include, there is a spiritual something in him which seems to go out to meet these qualities and contents, whilst they seem to come in to be received by it. It is what welcomes or rejects. It presides over the perception of sensations, and by giving or withholding its assent it influences the movements they tend to arouse. It is the home of interest.[3]

James argues against the proposition that this Self exists. He holds that the thought in one's mind at the present instant of time establishes a continuity with previous thoughts by selectively appropriating to its content aspects of these previous thoughts with the result that the present thought gains the impression of a Self continuing in time. James believes:

> Thought entirely unconscious of itself in the act of thinking . . . would be a firm basis on which the consciousness of personal identity would rest.

And he goes on to reject the need for a Thinker.

> Such consciousness, then, as a psychologic fact, can be fully described without supposing any other agent than a succession of perishing thoughts, endowed with the functions of appropriation and rejection. . . .[4]

> "Thought"—a cognitive phenomenal event in time—is, if it exists at all, itself the only Thinker the facts require.[5]

James holds that whenever one searches one's mind for evidence of a Self as the Thinker one only finds thoughts about

Self and the Thinker and these thoughts represent the basic relevant "facts" of introspection. He therefore rejects the concept of Self, the Thinker, as an unnecessary illusion akin to the concept of the Soul which he calls a "complete super-fluity, so far as accounting for the actually verified facts of conscious experience goes." * 6

An additional objection that James has to the spiritualistic concept of Soul is that the term, as it is used, carries the connotation of immortality. But James adds:

> The reader who finds any comfort in the idea of the Soul, is, however, perfectly free to continue to believe in it; for our reasonings have not established the non-existence of the Soul; they have only proved its superfluity for scientific purposes.[7]

Rene Descartes, philosopher and mathematician, (1596–1650) tried to establish by logic the existence of his "self" (which he identified with his soul): "I think therefore I am." In responding to his critics he admitted that this argument does not qualify as rigorous logic because it lacks the premise that all thinking things exist. He goes on to argue that his "self" exists because it is known to him as a direct experience.

My sensations, emotions, and thoughts are mental phenomena in my field of consciousness. Although they are known to me as subjective experiences, they are nevertheless phenomena of nature because I am an entity in nature and all phenomena in me are phenomena in nature. I directly, subjectively, sense my "self" in the acts of critically considering the information coming to my mind, wondering about it, and directing my thought processes in an attempt to arrive at a conclusion concerning this information that is acceptable to me. Through my sense experiences, I am aware of my body

---

* Hume in *Treatise of Human Nature* (I, iv, 6) said that mind is "nothing but a bundle or collection of different perceptions which succeed each other with an inconceivable rapidity, and are in perpetual flux and movement."

and of the movement of many of its parts (some of which I can control), and of its hurts. My self may be inspired to compose a poem or a song, or to paint a picture, or to guide my thoughts in the analysis of a philosophical question. This self, the core of my sense of being, known to me by direct experience, is my primary reality. I view self as a special NOME, different from the NOMEs projected by science, on the basis that it subjectively experiences mental events and can activate mental and bodily processes.

The Objective World

My purpose in this book as stated previously, is to explore relations between mind and body that reflect current findings in physical science and neurology. Consistent with this purpose is the basic assumption I call "the anatomical premise," which holds that I am configured as described by the neuroscientist and physiologist. This is, in effect, an assumption that the objective world exists. My belief that this is valid is strengthened by the fact that the information provided to me by my sensory systems is in consonance with the anatomical premise.

Neuroscientists describe sensory systems in my eyes, ears, nose, fingers, and so forth, which send information to my brain. When I stand in front of a mirror, I see the mirror and my image in it. The image of my body agrees with the scientific description of it. As I slowly close my eyes and see the image of them close, the image slowly fades. When I strike the mirror lightly with a key held in my hand, my ears report the noise of the impact at the same time that my eyes and fingers report this event. In the course of operating in the objective world I am flooded with information reflecting a similar mutual consistency of sensory signals. Should any of my sensory systems malfunction I consult a physician, who attempts to correct the defect employing the available scientific knowledge on the structure and processes of my body. I find that I must deal with things in the objective world in terms of their characteristics. I cannot walk through a stone wall.

A key component of the brain and the nervous systems that connect the brain to the sensory organs is the neuron, which like a telegraph line, transmits information in the form of sequences of electrical impulses. The brain contains 100 billion neurons, extensively interconnected. While we know that the modality of the mental experience depends on where in the brain the electrical impulses from the sensory organs are received, we do not understand the process whereby electrical activity is transduced into mental experiences. When one sees and hears a soldier beating a drum there is no actual picture of the soldier nor the sound of a drumbeat physically produced in the brain. When one is aware of the odor of perfume, the electrical impulses received by the brain from the nose do not cause perfume to spray in the brain. The actual picture, sound, and odor exist only as mental experiences.

The mental experiences generated as a result of the impact of signals from the objective world, like the picture and sound of the drummer, can be readily distinguished from other mental content such as emotions and thoughts because they are presented to the mind as coming from some specific place outside the brain.

Because the data provided by my sensory systems are in consonance with the scientific description of these systems, and because the things I perceive in the objective world must be dealt with in accordance with their characteristics whenever I encounter them, I have judged that the objective world belongs, along with my "self," in the category of items that define reality for me.

The Vocabulary of Mental Events

A list of words have, over the years, come into use, that relate to mental experiences. These words allow people, who have had similar kinds of mental experiences, to communicate with understanding about these experiences, even though these words defy definition in objective terms.

Two men, observing a rainbow in the sky, can communicate with understanding concerning their pleasure in seeing the multicolored display, even though they cannot describe in objective terms the experience of color. The story goes, that a man tried to describe the color red to a friend, who was born blind. After a lengthy exposition the blind man finally said: "Now I understand. It is like the sound of a trumpet."

Similar remarks can be made about a host of other words denoting mental experiences, like odor, red, light, sound, pain, fear, love, that have to be experienced to be really understood.

Reality

The ideas on reality distributed throughout this chapter will be now summarized. Reality is one of the class of words that defies definition in objective terms. The Random House Unabridged Dictionary, for example, provides the following definitions. Reality: "Something that exists. . . ." Exist: "To have actual being." Being: "The fact of existing." No objective criterion is offered for distinguishing being from nonbeing. Nor is philosophy or science helpful in this regard. Philosopher Martin Heidegger, who has written extensively in the field of ontology, in his essay "On Time and Being" says: "Being proves to be destiny's gift of presence, the gift granted by the giving of time." In the words of scientist Werner Heisenberg: "Science no longer confronts nature as an objective observer but sees itself as an actor in the interplay between man and nature." [8]

In the absence of precise objective criteria, each person defines reality for himself or herself by the items he or she places into the category of the real after a critical assessment of (1) personal experiences and perceptions, and (2) information, both spoken and written, provided by other people. One would tend to discount one's perceptions which one viewed as having been experienced while dreaming or hallucinating. One might accept the statement of an astronaut, who had visited the moon, that the moon is composed of rocks and not of green cheese. One might reject, or possibly accept, the statement of a man, who said he talked to an angel, as evidence for the existence of angels.

This definition of reality allows for some difference in the conception of reality by different people. It reflects human limitations for perceiving and knowing. There may be realms of being completely beyond human conception.

I have learned to associate certain of my sensory experiences with material things in the objective world. From the behavior of these material things science has inferred the existence of nonmaterial dynamisms, hidden essences that imbed and implement the laws of nature. Both the material things and the nonmaterial dynamisms of the objective world are included in my category of the real. I view the body of scientific laws as a useful device conceived by the minds of physicists for predicting the behavior of material objects and not as the actual dynamism that implements this behavior.

Because other people report sensory experiences essentially similar to mine when encountering the same physical objects, I conclude that the objective world has a being that transcends my perception of it.

I view my personal dynamism, my self, which can aspire and drive my thoughts and actions toward the fulfillment of these aspirations, as a nonmaterial essence that has at least the same level of reality as the nonmaterial dynamisms that activate material things according to the laws of physical science.

On States of Consciousness

In the normal course of life one encounters several ordinary states of consciousness in wakefulness, sleep, and
dreaming. David Shapiro[9] suggests that the nature of human
consciousness may change in time.

> Whether or not the anatomy of the nervous system is still evolv-
> ing, there is meaning in the evolution of consciousness. It is a
> social process in which natural occurring tendencies are selected
> out of a total set of possibilities. It is a matter of individual ex-
> perience and cultural definition which can probably alter the na-
> ture of consciousness considerably in the same sense that social
> views, intuition, and language usage are constantly producing
> new conceptions of reality.

Hypnosis, transcendental meditation, and the ingestion of
psychedelic drugs induce special altered states of consciousness. Psychologists Robert Ornstein[10] and Charles Tart[11] hold
that in these states one's mind is free of the domination of the
logical, noisy side of the brain, with the result that the intuitive, holistic side may be heard, and may lead one to new
truths. Tart further suggests that during the altered state of
consciousness one may experience a new state of being in
which one achieves a deeper insight into reality. This experience may provide an appreciation of the views of the Eastern
mystics regarding the oneness of all objects and all minds in
nature.

Some Unusual Concepts of Reality

The philosopher Wilhelm Hegel (1770–1831) proposed
the view that all minds and all objects are united in a common entity which he calls the "Absolute." The Absolute is
self-conscious, and all history flows out of it.

Because of the strange behavior of subatomic particles, as
indicated by quantum mechanics, which cannot be explained

from the purview of the present scientific model of nature, many physicists are searching for a new model. Fritjof Capra[12] proposes that the scientific view of nature is shifting toward that of the Eastern mystics, namely, that all minds and all objects are conjoined in a "oneness."

Physicist David Bohm[13] places this oneness of all minds and things in a higher realm of being which he calls the "Implicate Order," and which is time-less and space-less. The Implicate Order is the true reality. The world of familiar experience, which he calls the "Explicate Order," is an illusion, a projection from the Implicate Order. This concept will be discussed in chapter 14.

Marilyn Ferguson[14] summarizes the literature on the search for a new paradigm of nature which highlights the trend in some scientific and philosophic thought toward Eastern mysticism.

On the Modeling of Mind

The advent of the electronic computer has made it possible to simulate many of the processes of the mind mechanistically. Employing an electronic computer and additional electronic equipment it is possible, for example, to construct a machine that, when impacted by certain molecules emanating from a rose, says "I detect the fragrance of a rose." And there is nothing in the theories of physical science that precludes the possibility of making a machine that could detect all the odors perceived by man. It is also conceivable that a machine could be built that would respond correctly to all the other of man's sensory inputs. Machines have been built that play expert games of checkers and chess, solve difficult mathematical problems, and perform other "thought" processes that were once considered to be the unique capability of the human mind. Physical science projects the promise that whatever process can be described in objective terms can be modeled at least in concept by a mechanistic device.

For these reasons many scientists believe that the brain is, in effect, a mechanistic device that handles all the functions formerly attributed to the mind and that beyond the brain and its processes there is no mind as a discrete entity.

What has been ignored by these scientists is the matter of subjective experience. Their science provides no basis for the possibility that an assembly of atoms of the proper configuration can introspectively experience subjective phenomena. When a man perceives the odor of a rose he is aware subjectively of the pleasant, enjoyable fragrance of the rose. It is only through such subjective experiences that humans know odor, sound, and light, whereas scientists, if they lacked these subjective experiences, would know only special molecules, air vibrations, and photons respectively. Through the urging and directing of their minds, scientists conceive their theories, composers write their symphonies, and artists paint their pictures. The subjective drama provides one with the sense of being and of existing in this world.

Scientists of the mechanistic persuasion tend to reject the concept of mind because there is no basis for subjectivity and its processes in their science. Where do the forces of mind come from and how are they imbedded in nature? The answer, of course, is that we do not know. But neither do the scientists know how the forces of gravity and electricity and their laws evolved and are imbedded in nature. In rejecting the reality of mind, scientists have cut nature down to their limits of understanding.

Chapter Three

On the Scientific Method

The Inductive Process

Scientists are confronted with a number of observations concerning the physical world, which they call empirical data. Although deductive logic has a place in the process of conceiving a theory relating to these data, it is inductive logic that plays the major role in this process. And it will be inductive logic that I will employ in my discussion of the mind and its interaction with the physical world.

The Random House Unabridged Dictionary defines induction as it relates to logic as "any form of reasoning in which the conclusion although supported by the premises does not follow from them necessarily." Conversely, in deductive logic the conclusion does necessarily follow from the premises.

Inductive logic is, for example, used by a jury in arriving at a verdict based on circumstantial evidence. A well-known politician was surrounded by a group of people in a hotel lobby. Witnesses saw a man standing near the politician produce a gun, aim it at the politician, fire, and the politician fell mortally wounded. Men in the crowd disarmed the gunman and held him for the police. At the alleged assassin's court trial his lawyer argued that the defendant's bullet missed its mark, but that another gunman standing in an obscure part of the lobby fired the lethal bullet at the same instant. No one saw the bullet leave the defendant's gun and enter the victim's body, nor was any evidence brought that it was indeed that bullet that killed the victim. The jury brought a verdict of guilty as charged against the defendant.

But this verdict represented an exercise of judgment in which the jury chose to discount the lawyer's scenario as highly improbable although they could not hold that it was impossible.

With regard to the conception of scientific theories, physicist Max Born says:

> There is no logical path from fact to theory. Power of imagination, intuition, fantasy are here, as everywhere, the sources of creative achievement, and the criterion of correctness is represented by the power of predicting phenomena that have not yet been investigated or discovered.[1]

Once a theory is expressed as a mathematical equation deductive logic can be effectively employed. Mathematical manipulation of the equation, which is an exercise in deductive logic, may lead to important new insights into nature. The ability of a theory to provide new insights, as Born points out, is some indication of the correctness of the theory. However, even if a theory does correctly predict some new phenomena, this success does not guarantee the adequacy of the theory for all phenomena the future might disclose. Einstein's theory of general relativity, for example, made some very impressive predictions and yet proved inadequate in the subatomic regime where quantum mechanics applies.

Obviously the inductive process is not a precise method of analysis. The answers given by the inductive process depend on human intuition. It is not a process that can be programmed on a computer.

These remarks on the inductive process in science and its limitations are illustrated by the following brief account taken from the history of scientific discovery.

Examples of the Inductive Process in Science

Johann Kepler (1571–1630) tried to confirm the then radical Copernican theory that the planets revolve about the sun by analyzing the existing data on the planetary orbits. His first assumption, that the planetary orbits were perfect circles with the sun at the center, did not exactly agree with the orbital data. He then worked on the assumption that the orbits were elliptical with the sun at one of the focuses of the ellipse and was satisfied with the agreement of these orbits with the available data. He noted that a planet moves at different speeds at different points in its orbit, but that a line drawn from the sun to the planet sweeps out equal areas in equal time intervals at all points in the orbit; this observation is known as Kepler's law. Although Kepler's efforts contributed much to the advancement of science, they represent only a limited exercise of creative imagination.

Newton, less than a century later, confronted by essentially similar astronomical data, possessed the imaginative power to conceive the laws of mechanics and gravitation. Newton's laws may be used not only to predict planetary orbits but also to predict the paths of projectiles and satellites, the motion of machine components and, in general, the motion of macroscopic objects in response to gravitational and mechanistic forces.

Unfortunately, Newton's base of data was incomplete. Albert Michelson and E. W. Morley, at the end of the nineteenth century, demonstrated experimentally that the speed of light as perceived by any given observer is constant regardless of the magnitude of the velocity of that observer relative to the source of light. This one discovery called for a major revision of the laws of mechanics. As the interest of science expanded in the directions of both the microscopic and the cosmic regimes, Newtonian mechanics was found to become increasingly deficient.

Einstein, employing innovative approaches to the handling of gravity, space, and time, conceived the general theory of relativity, which does take account of the invariance of the speed of light. Einstein's equation of general relativity is not derivable deductively from Newton's equations and the fact that the speed of light is constant. It involves a radically different view of nature. The cosmos is pictured as a four-dimensional continuum in space and time which is warped in the vicinity of physical objects. One marvels at the mental process that led to the conception of the general theory of relativity. In reflecting on his creative efforts, Einstein declared: "The really valuable thing is intuition."

The theory of relativity expands scientific insight into the phenomena of nature. It predicts, for example, the bending of light by gravitational fields, the possible existence of black holes, and the difference in the passage of time on the earth and on a satellite sent into orbit around the earth. It, however, does not represent the ultimate description of nature. It was necessary for Erwin Schrodinger to conceive the equations of quantum mechanics to describe the probabilistic aspects of the behavior of subatomic particles. A theory that combines general relativity and quantum mechanics is now being sought. And it is possible that new discoveries may require further revision of these theories.

Much of the current philosophical discourse on nature tends to take the theories of quantum mechanics and general relativity as ultimate descriptions of nature. The possibility, as Einstein's letter to Cousins suggests, his theory may in time be displaced by new theories, which may call for radically new conceptions in natural philosophy, is often overlooked.

On the Logic Processes in Natural Philosophy

A philosophical inquiry into nature also must start with a set of observations on things and phenomena in nature. And, as in science, so also in philosophy, any attempt to conceive a theory that provides a consistent, unified, grounding for these observations must proceed by inductive logic employing inspired intuition and judgment. The subsequent investigation of a proposed theory to test its relevance, to improve its logical consistency, and to explore its implications are exercises in deductive logic.

In the process of assembling the primary data the philosopher must include observations on phenomena in both the objective and subjective domains. And he must not discard evidence of interactions between these domains because these interactions cannot be explained by current science.

The various philosophical theories, even the conflicting theories, concerning nature are of interest and importance because they reveal some of the aspects of this extremely complex matter. In spite of the claims in some of these philosophical dissertations to irrefutable exercises in deductive logic, critical examination discloses that they are merely carefully considered opinions advanced by very bright and imaginative minds.

Some of these theories, the radical materialistic theories, like behaviorism, relate to the materialistic realm of nature. Other of these theories, the idealistic theories as advanced by George Berkeley, relate to the nonmaterial realm of nature. But, as pointed out in chapter 1, science reveals the existence of both the material and nonmaterial realms of being. This fact is recognized in some philosophies and its implications will be explored in this book.

Part Two

The Body As A
Matter-Energy System

Chapter Four

The Enigma of Matter

Matter as Perceived Properties

The entire cosmos, in the eyes of the physicist, is a system of matter-energy, and the human body, which is a component of the cosmos, shares this characterization. But what is matter?

One tends to view an item of matter in terms of its properties. A given piece of ice, for example, is a one inch cube, having a weight of roughly half an ounce. It is nearly colorless and is cold, hard, and smooth to the touch. Is the ice cube simply the combination of these properties, or is there a substrate that underlies and embodies these properties?

The shape, size, color, smoothness, and temperature are all properties discerned by dealing with the external surface of the ice cube. The weight or mass of the ice cube is equal to the force of gravity acting on it as measured by a scale. Obviously the substance of the ice cube is not merely the sum of these properties.

If man were endowed with radically different perceptive systems, or if his culture were not scientifically oriented, he would characterize the ice cube in terms of different properties.

Furthermore, if the ice cube is heated so that now it becomes a pool of water its physical properties change drastically. Even the weight changes.* An additional change in

---

* According to Einstein's relation between energy and mass, when the energy of an object is increased by heating it, its mass and, hence, weight increase.

properties occurs when the water is heated to form a cloud of steam.

Yet, in spite of all these changes in properties, it is considered that one is still dealing with the same basic substance. The philosopher John Locke (1632–1704), after attempting to identify the substrate that supports the properties of matter, concludes it is "something we know not what." [1]

The Inner Structure of Matter

A physicist would hold that what remains invariant during these several changes in the state of the ice cube is the kind and number of atoms contained therein. A given ice cube has specific numbers of atoms of hydrogen and oxygen in the ratio of two atoms of hydrogen to one atom of oxygen. Hydrogen and oxygen are composed of what were, in the early part of the twentieth century, believed to be the building blocks of all matter, namely, electrons, protons, and neutrons. An oxygen atom consists of eight protons and eight neutrons tightly bound together to form its nucleus, and eight electrons in orbit around the nucleus like planets around the sun. The hydrogen atom has a nucleus composed of one proton, and it has one electron in orbit around its nucleus.

The chemical identity of an atom is determined by the number of protons in its nucleus. Hydrogen has one proton in its nucleus, helium has two, lithium has three, beryllium has four, boron has five, carbon has six, nitrogen has seven, oxygen has eight, and so forth. There are somewhat over one hundred known kinds of atoms that are called elements.

An electron possesses a negative electric charge. A proton possesses an equal positive charge. Particles with like charges repel one another; particles with unlike charges attract one another. A normal atom which has as many electrons in orbit around its nucleus as it has protons in its nucleus is electrically in balance. If it has more electrons than protons, the atom has a·net negative electrical charge and is called a negative ion. If there is a deficiency of electrons relative to protons the atom has a net positive charge and is called a positive ion.

Currently physicist Murray Gell-Mann proposes that the proton and neutron consist of various numbers of two types of more fundamental particles called quarks. The proton is said to consist of two μ quarks and one d quark and the neutron of one μ quark and two d quarks. The electron and the quarks are at present believed to be fundamental particles in the sense that they cannot be subdivided.

In the structure and processes of the human body we are concerned with no subdivision of matter below the atom and its ions and the electron. The body is composed of extremely complex assemblies of atoms of carbon, hydrogen, oxygen, nitrogen, sodium, potassium, calcium, and very small but essential amounts of other elements.

Let us now return to the question: What is matter? Particles of matter, such as electrons, protons, and neutrons, are characterized by various of the parameters of mass, electric charge, spin, and so on. The most significant of these parameters is mass, because while a particle may not possess all these parameters, if it lacks mass it is not a particle of matter.

What is mass? Mass in the sense that it is used by the physicist is a number derived from an equation conceived by the human mind. Or in the words of Born: "In physics . . . we must strongly emphasize the word mass has no meaning other than that given by formula (6)."[2] According to the theory of relativity, the mass of an object depends on its velocity. And the velocity of an object cannot be specified until an observer arrives on the scene and sets a frame of reference with respect to which the velocity of the object is measured. A description of the cosmos in terms of its mass distribution likewise is not possible until an observer sets a frame of reference. After considering the various theories, and from his

---

* Formula (6) states that mass is equal to the impulse applied to an object divided by its resultant change in velocity.

insight into the relation between the theories of quantum mechanics and the behavior of the subatomic particles of nature, Heisenberg was moved to write: "Science no longer confronts nature as an objective observer but sees itself as an actor in the interplay between man and nature." [3] Neither our direct sensory perception of the properties of physical objects nor the description of their fundamental components in terms of numbers derived from the equations of science has led us to a conception of matter as a thing-in-itself. We cannot even imagine what we need to know to satisfy our minds that we know matter as a thing-in-itself. We must, therefore, acknowledge that our perceptive and cognitive capabilities are limited, and echo Locke's statement that matter or substance is "something we know not what." We can, nonetheless, deal operationally with the behavior of matter employing our knowledge of its properties and the equations of science.

Chapter Five

Limits in the Scientific Understanding of Energy

On Force

Mathematical physics, a powerful tool for investigating and predicting the course of physical phenomena, virtually began with the equations proposed by Newton. These equations appeared to feature force as a primary reality in nature.

From his studies of the data relating to the motion of the planets around the sun, Newton concluded that between two bodies there exists a force of attraction (the gravitational force) which is equal to the product of the masses of these bodies divided by the square of the distance between them. He also proposed that the force required to accelerate a body is equal to the mass of the body multiplied by its acceleration. If no force was applied to a body then, according to Newton, it would move in a straight line at constant velocity. He also said that for every action there is an equal and opposite reaction.

Newton's equations provide the means for computing not only the motion of planets but also the motion of other physical objects like mechanical devices, satellites, and projectiles.

It was already known in Newton's time that there were other force manifestations than gravity. William Gilbert (1544–1603), observed that when one rubbed certain objects together, like a glass rod and a silk handkerchief, these objects exhibited properties of attraction and repulsion. He proposed that there existed two kinds of electricity and that objects charged with the same kind of electricity repelled each other, while objects charged with unlike kinds of electricity attracted each other.* Two centuries later C. A. Coulomb (1736–1806) proposed the law known as Coulomb's Law; namely, that the force of attraction, or repulsion, between two objects is equal to the product of their charges divided by the square of the distance between them.

Ernest Rutherford (1871–1936) proposed a concept of the structure of the atom which evolved (with the subsequent discovery of the neutron) into the present concept. The atom consists of negatively charged electrons, positively charged protons, and neutrons possessing zero charge. The charges on each of the electrons and protons are quantitatively equal but with the stated difference designated by sign. The forces between these charged particles are orders of magnitude greater than the gravitational attraction between them based on their masses. The protons and neutrons of an atom form a very compact nucleus that contains most of the mass of the atom. The electrons orbit around the nucleus held in their orbits by the force of electrical attraction between them and the protons in the nucleus.

To counter the mutual force of repulsion between the protons in the nucleus, which, if unopposed would tend to disintegrate the nucleus, it was necessary to propose a short range force within the nucleus called the "strong force." The strong force is orders of magnitude greater than the electric force and binds together the protons and neutrons in the nucleus.

In addition there is a "weak force," manifest in interactions involving neutrinos that are released in nuclear processes.

Without the electric and strong forces, all matter would break down into electrons, protons, and neutrons. It is therefore these forces that are responsible for structuring the animate and inanimate objects of the cosmos.

* Benjamin Franklin supplied the terms *positive* and *negative* to differentiate those forms of electricity.

A moving electric force field, as created for example by the motion of electrons in a wire, generates a magnetic force field. This field is capable of deflecting the magnetic needle of a compass, and magnetic objects in general, from which effect comes the name for this force. Because the magnetic force is created by the electric force in motion, it is not considered a separate fundamental force. Instead we refer to the electrostatic and the magnetic forces as different manifestations of an electromagnetic force concept.

Thus at present there are identified four forces, namely, the gravitational, electromagnetic, strong, and weak. And it is entirely possible that further research may result in the proposal of other forces.

Einstein had hoped to develop a unified field theory in which the various forces represent special manifestations of a common force concept. But he was unsuccessful in this endeavor. Physicists, still working toward this objective, have recently shown that the electromagnetic and weak forces are related.

Replacement of Force by Energy as a Reality of Nature

Is force a reality of nature or is it a concept invented by scientists? Concerning gravitational force Newton said:

> That one body may act upon another at a distance through a vacuum without the mediation of anything else, by and through which their action and force may be conveyed from one to another, is to me so greatly an absurdity that I believe no man, who has in philosophical matters a competent faculty of thinking, can ever fall into it.[1]

Newton further states in his letters to Bentley that what causes objects to behave as if there were a force of gravity attracting them together is a mystery to him.

After an extensive study of the various attempts by physicists, mathematicians, and philosophers to find a physical basis for force, Max Jammer stated:

> Since the time of Keill and Berkeley, it became increasingly clear that the concept of force, if divested of all its extrascientific connotations, reveals itself as an empty scheme, a pure relational or mathematical function.[2]

Instead of force, energy is now being regarded as the real entity in nature. Force is considered to be a useful mathematically defined term.*

The Genesis of Energy

The concept of energy, as it is understood and used by physicists, had its genesis in Newton's equations. Manipulation of these equations provided a formulation in which the force terms were absent and two terms appeared which seemed to have special significance.

One of these terms, *kinetic energy,* is expressed as one half the mass of a body multiplied by its velocity squared. The other energy term, *gravitational potential energy,* is expressed as the product of the masses of two bodies divided by the distance between them (measured from their centers of gravity), and it has a negative sign associated with it.**

The reason these two terms acquired special significance is that in any given process to which Newton's equations apply and during which process the two terms are changing, the

---

* In Newtonian mechanics the force on an object of constant mass, for example, is equal to the rate of change of its energy (kinetic or potential) with respect to distance, taken in a special direction.

** Gravitational potential energy is the energy two bodies are said to have when they are separated. This energy is a maximum when the two bodies are separated by an infinite distance. It is convenient and conventional to compute these energy values with respect to the value at infinite separation distance. The values at distances less than infinite therefore carry a negative sign.

sum of the two terms remains constant. For example, in the orbiting of a comet around the sun, as the comet comes closer to the sun thereby suffering a decrease in gravitational potential energy, it acquires a higher velocity, hence a higher kinetic energy. But the sum of the two energies remains the same at every point in the comet's orbit.

As the physicist's list of energies grew to include heat energy and the various manifestations of electromagnetic energy, it was found that when these energies are also taken into account, the total energy involved in any process remains constant even though the individual energies change. This empirical fact is the basis for the pronouncement of the law of conservation of energy.

Einstein showed that there is an equivalence between energy and mass in accordance with the equation $E = mC^2$, where C is the velocity of light. With this added insight the conservation law became the law of conservation of mass-energy. Because of its apparent indestructibility mass-energy was deemed to be a hard fact of nature. And since mass is a parameter of matter, the cosmos is currently viewed as a system of matter-energy.

In the fourteenth century, William of Ockham proposed the rule "Plurality is not to be assumed without necessity." This rule is now called Ockham's razor.* It is applied by scientists in their efforts to reduce to a minimum the basic entities and laws needed to describe nature; the goal is a single building block and a single law. With energy emerging as a basic entity of nature, scientists, applying Ockham's razor, are relegating force to the status of a mathematically defined quantity. Newton's laws can be stated mathematically as was shown by Ernst Mach, Gustav Kirkhoff, and Heinrich Hertz, without involving the concept of force. Einstein's equation of general relativity does not contain force as a term.

* It is also known as Occam's Razor.

Heat Energy

Heat energy is related to kinetic energy in the sense that it is a measure of the energies associated with the motions of the large number of particles that constitute a volume of gas or liquid or a solid object. In a quantity of helium, for example, confined within a container, the atoms of helium move about at random velocities and these velocities change with time as the atoms collide with one another and with the walls of the container. The kinetic energy of any one atom is thus continuously changing. But if the container is insulated to prevent the loss of heat, then the total kinetic energy of all the helium atoms within the container remains constant. The heat energy is a measure of this total kinetic energy.

In a volume of gas in which each molecule consists of two or more atoms, appreciable contributions to the heat energy come not only from the linear motions of the molecules but also from their rotational motions and from the vibrational motions of the atoms within the structure of each molecule. In solids the atoms are largely constrained to oscillate around their respective sites in the matrix of the solid; the greater the velocity of these atoms the greater is their mean kinetic energies and the greater is the value of the heat energy said to be contained within the solid.

As previously pointed out, the law of conservation of mass-energy requires that the higher the heat content of a given ensemble of particles, the higher is the total effective mass of that ensemble.

Electrical Energy

There is an energy called "electrical potential energy" that is determined by the charge strengths of electrically charged objects and the distances between these objects. For example, the electrical potential energy credited to two electrons is equal to the product of the amounts of charge on the electrons divided by the distance between them. If these two electrons are free to move, they would fly apart, and as the separation distance increased, their potential energy would decrease and the sum of their kinetic energies would increase by an equal amount with the result that the total energy would remain constant.

This electrical energy is not associated physically with the electrons, because if either electron is prevented from moving, the energy shows up in the movement of the free electron. And it exists even if the space between and around the electrons is a vacuum. Therefore, this energy lies in the nonmaterial realm of being.

It should be noted that this energy term is not sufficient to determine the performance of the electrons. It is one term in another equation (e.g., Hamilton's equation) that takes into account the initial kinetic energies of the electrons and which must be manipulated toward a solution in order to calculate the paths of the electrons. The several equations must be viewed as the scientist's attempt to model the performance of the nonmaterial essence that is actually interacting with the physical particles and with the other energies. The means whereby these interactions are implemented are hidden from human perception and are a profound mystery. These observations hold also for other energy forms (e.g., gravitational energy).

Electrical energy is also manifest in a vibratory mode, namely, as vibratory electromagnetic (EM) waves that travel at a speed of 186,000 miles per second. These EM waves occur in a wide range of vibratory frequencies. At the low frequency end of the spectrum are radiant heat waves. Higher in order of increasing vibratory frequency come the radio waves, the light waves, the X-rays, and finally at the high end of the spectrum come the gamma rays.

The existence of these EM waves is made manifest only by their effects on physical objects. The radiant heat waves cause an increase in temperature of the objects on which they impinge. In the radio wave range the waves are detected by special electrical equipment. Light waves are detected when they knock electrons out of special chemicals in the neurons of the eye, which send electrical impulses to the brain where they produce the mental experience of a flash of light. X-rays and gamma rays are detected by their effects when they strike special scientific instruments. These EM waves are events in the nonmaterial essence that mediates electrical phenomena.

The Particle Concept of EM Waves

Newton suggested that light is composed of particles. Christian Huygens, a contemporary of Newton, on the basis of his experiments in optics, proposed the alternative view that light is a wave phenomenon. The wave concept readily explains the behavior of light beams as they are reflected by mirrors of various shapes and as they are diffracted in passing through lenses and prisms, and the interference patterns formed when two beams of the same frequency but out of phase with each other shine on the same spot.

The wave theory was the dominant concept until the end of the nineteenth century. Max Planck (1858–1947) proposed that the energy that forms EM waves is released by matter as lumps or quanta. These quanta or particles of EM energy are called photons. Einstein suggested that when an EM wave interacts with subatomic particles, for example electrons, it behaves as if it were an assembly of photons. A photon of the proper energy acting like a billiard ball can knock an electron out of its orbit in an atom.

A single model that accounts for both the wave and particulate aspects of EM waves has not yet been conceived. The wave model is usually employed in problems in optics and the particulate model is used in problems in atomic physics. The energy of a photon is related to the frequency of vibration of the EM wave of which it is a component; the photon energy is equal to the frequency multiplied by a number called Planck's constant.

Some Energy Interactions

The hydrogen atom is the simplest of the atoms. It consists of one electron in orbit around the nucleus of the atom, which is one proton. The ideas presented for this atom hold also for the more complex atoms.

The total energy of the electron, in orbit around the proton is the sum of its kinetic energy (determined by the velocity of the electron) and the electrical potential energy (determined by the distance of the electron from the proton). The distance of the electron orbit from the proton depends on the magnitude of this total energy; the lower this energy the closer is the orbit to the proton. It was once believed that all energies and hence all orbital distances were possible. But it was later found that only a discrete set of energies and the associated orbital distances were permitted by nature. This set of energies may be calculated employing Schrodinger's wave equation.

It was found empirically that an electron can jump from its orbit to one in which its energy is lower, and its loss in energy shows up as a photon of equal energy. Thus an energy change related to changes in position and velocity of the electron is transmuted into a photon of vibratory electromagnetic energy. The production of this photon, a nonmaterial entity, is mediated by the NOME that handles electrical phenomena. The photon may possibly be an energetic disturbance in this exciter.

There is nothing about the electrical field of the electron or the proton of the hydrogen atom as specified by the equation that defines electric fields or about the parameters of these particles that suggest the possibility of the orbital restrictions projected by Schrodinger's equation. These orbital restrictions must be imposed by the aforementioned NOME.

A photon of the proper energy, impacting on a piece of matter, can knock an electron out of its orbit in one of the atoms of that matter. The energy of the photon is decreased by the amount of energy required to remove the electron from its orbit and provide the kinetic energy of the electron in its freed state. This loss in energy of the photon is reflected in a corresponding reduction in the vibratory frequency of the photon. This phenomenon is called the Compton effect.

When a photon of sufficient energy strikes a metallic plate, it can knock an electron out of that plate and disappear. The energy of the photon is consumed to offset the energy that binds the electron to the structure of the plate and to provide the kinetic energy of the freed electron. This phenomenon is called the photoelectric effect.

The photoelectric and Compton effects illustrate the transference of photon energy to kinetic and potential energy.

Transmutation of Energy into Mass

One or more gamma photons are produced when the nucleus of a uranium or plutonium atom captures a neutron and fissions. A gamma photon may lose energy by knocking electrons out of atoms that it encounters. A gamma photon having an energy of 1.02 million electron volts can disappear and in its place an electron and a positron are born. The relation between the amount of energy lost and the amount of mass produced is given by Einstein's equation, namely, the energy lost is equal to the mass gained multiplied by the velocity of light squared. (A positron is the antiparticle to an electron; it has the same mass as the electron but the opposite electric charge.)

The inverse transmutation can also occur. When an electron and a positron meet, both can vanish and two gamma photons appear each having an energy of half the energy of the photon that produced the electron-positron pair.

The transmutation of energy into matter is mediated by

the essence in the nonmaterial realm. This raises the interesting question: Is the nonmaterial realm the conduit whereby energy, and from that energy matter, were introduced into the universe? The full capabilities of the nonmaterial realm have not yet been revealed. Before the twentieth century, instruments capable of detecting gamma photons had not yet been developed and scientists were not aware of the existence of these photons. Gamma rays, undetected, nonetheless could do much harm to body tissue.

The Cosmos as a Matter-Energy System

Up until at least the end of the nineteenth century, science projected the belief that the cosmos could, in theory, be described objectively by specifying the distribution of all the matter and energy in the system. In the previous chapter it was pointed out that in the twentieth century, with the advent of the theory of relativity, this belief is no longer valid. It was realized that the mass of an object, the essential parameter of matter, depends for its value on the velocity with which the object is moving and could not be specified until an observer sets a frame of reference with respect to which the velocity is measured.

A similar limitation applies to various of the energy terms. The kinetic energy of an object depends on the mass and velocity of the object (it is equal to one half the mass multiplied by the velocity squared). It is evident that a frame of reference must be established before the kinetic energy of an object can be computed.

Two observers moving at different velocities with respect to the source of an electromagnetic wave will record on their instruments different vibrational frequencies for this wave. And since the energy of each of the photons that constitute the wave depends on this vibrational frequency, the observers will report different energy values for these photons.

Let us suppose that one could perform the impossible feat

of specifying the magnitudes and the distribution of all the masses and energies in the universe at some given point in time, this would still not represent an adequate description of the universe. The masses and energies, if I may be permitted an imperfect analogy, may be viewed as sheep without a shepherd. What is missing from this mass-energy representation of the universe is the NOME which embodies and implements the laws that govern the interactions and changes with time of these masses and energies. These laws are inferred by scientists from observations on the behavior of objects, and are usually represented in science by mathematical equations. How they are embodied and implemented is hidden from human perception.

This deficiency in human perception should be remembered in the discussion of consciousness.

Chapter Six

A Basic Mystery Attending the Laws of Nature

The Miracle of the "Bridge"

In spite of the fact that we do not know, in any absolute objective sense, what matter and energy are, nevertheless science has discovered laws that permit the prediction of changes with time of those manifestations of matter and energy that are available to our perception.

Newton's laws of mechanics, for example, allow the prediction of the motion of objects in gravitational force fields. Einstein, in his general theory of relativity, provides a more powerful predictive method that avoids the concept of force.

If a scientist desires to predict the orbit of a comet that has just been detected in our solar system, he must take measurements of the distance of the comet from the sun and the various planets and its velocity at the same instant in time. He must also have determined the masses of the sun and the planets. With this information entered into either Newton's or Einstein's equations, he can now predict the position and velocity of the comet at all other times as it orbits through our solar system.

But nature uses no astronomers, no equations, and no computers. Somehow the masses, positions, and velocities of all objects in nature are sensed and, what is stranger still in conformity with these parameters, the objects are directed into their proper courses without the aid of any means discernible to the scientist. With reference to this mystery, Jammer says:

In a certain sense, therefore, the acceleration of an object, from the point of view of classical physics, may be regarded as a miracle. Apart from the purely mathematical relation there is no "bridge" that leads from "configuration" to "accelerated motion."

. . . even in Einstein's general relativity, the miracle . . . has not yet disappeared: It has been transferred . . . to a different plane. It lies now in the functional relation between the space-time structure and the mass-energy distribution.[1]

Some Implications of the Miracle of the "Bridge"

Our failure to understand the "bridge" between, for example, the position of objects relative to one another and their resultant accelerations indicates either a basic deficiency in human perceptive capabilities or in the evolving scientific conception of the cosmos. Science's reliance on mathematical equations, a product of the mind, as a surrogate for a physical conception of this bridge led Sir James Jeans to remark:

In a completely objective survey of the situation the outstanding fact would seem to be that mechanics has already shot its bolt and has failed dismally on both the scientific and philosophical side. The universe begins to look more like a great thought than a great machine.[2]

The physicist's approach to nature through mathematical equations, that define the parameters of matter and energy and predict how they may change with time, is indeed a great thought—but it is human thought. These equations are not to be confused with nature. An equation is merely a set of ink marks on paper until it is engaged by a human mind that understands the meaning of its symbols, introduces the proper data into the equation, purposefully manipulates the equation toward a desired solution, and interprets the result.

The physicist attempts to build a paradigm of nature based on the entities defined by his equations. And in time, these entities take on an aura of reality because of the great predictive power of the associated equations. But, as indicated by Jeans, the validity of the current paradigms of nature based on physical science is breaking down. And this science is being revealed for what it is: a scheme devised by man to deal with the phenomena that engage his senses directly or with the aid of scientific instruments.

A similar thought is expressed by physicist Stephen W. Hawking in his book *A Brief History of Time*:

> you have to be clear what a scientific theory is. I shall take the simple-minded view that a theory is just a model of the universe, or a restricted part of it, and a set of rules that relate quantities in the model to observations that we make. It exists only in our minds and does not have any other reality (whatever that might mean).[3]

Science and Philosophy

The kind of descriptions of nature being provided by physical scientists is believed by many scientists and philosophers to represent the totality of nature. This belief has inspired such radical materialistic philosophies as behaviorism. These philosophies are classified as monistic.

But it must be emphasized, as pointed out in chapter 1, that, according to its scientific description, nature is actually dualistic. The scientific description calls for the existence of a material realm of being, and it posits a nonmaterial realm, the existence of which is inferred from the behavior of objects in the material realm. The content of the nonmaterial realm is represented by scientists as NOMEs like gravitational and electrical fields and their laws of interaction with matter, and these entities are the bridges that Jammer calls miracles.

Interaction between mind and brain has been a problem for the philosopher. But even in the world of the physical scientist, all interactions are mysterious. They are mediated by

NOMEs. The rebounding of two billiard balls after impacting is caused by the rejection of the atoms of each ball by the electric field of the other ball; no direct contact between the matter of the two balls occurs.

Physical science cannot claim that it has discovered all the NOMEs in nature. Nor can it disprove the theory that mind is a manifestation of a special nonmaterial essence that can interact with brain processes.

The NOME

The NOME incorporates, in some mysterious way, what physicists define mathematically as electric and gravitational fields and their interactions with material objects. The NOME that mediates electrical effects at the subatomic level of matter is modeled by the physicist in terms of the equations of quantum mechanics and Maxwell's equations (James Clark Maxwell 1831–1879). At the macroscopic level of matter the influence of quantum mechanics becomes negligible and only Maxwell's equations are significant.

But are Maxwell's equations sufficient for the whole macroscopic realm of matter? When we consider very complex molecules such as, for example, the genetic molecule of a bird, phenomena are observed which are difficult to explain employing solely Maxwell's equations. The genetic molecule of a bird is said to be the blueprint of its structure. But in all my years as an engineer, I have never seen a blueprint get off the desk and build the structure it represents. One can, at least in theory, conceive that Maxwell's equations alone are sufficient to explain the replication of portions of the genetic molecule to provide the various proteins that serve as the building blocks of the bird's structure. But somehow the genes cause these proteins to form the elaborate structure called the cell, to make various kinds of cells for feathers, skin, bones, tendons, muscles, heart, lungs, arteries, blood, nerves, glands, brain, viscera, wings, and so forth, to manufacture these cells in sufficient quantities and assemble them in proper configurations to form the various components of the bird. These components are proportioned, arranged, and interconnected so the bird may fly, walk, hunt for food, eat, avoid danger, grow, and reproduce. It appears to be far beyond the scope of Maxwell's equations, by themselves, to account for the translation of the structure of the genetic molecule into the bird, or for the mental capabilities the bird may possess.

It therefore seems reasonable to conclude that for very complex molecules the NOME possesses, in addition to the capability represented by Maxwell's equations, some incredible capabilities. Since in humans the NOME provides the capability for creative thought, it is conceivable that the NOME also possesses a mysterious kind of mentality.

The NOME is limited by the structure of a specific genetic molecule to construct a specific organism. Some people are born color blind because of a deficiency in their genetic molecules. When this deficiency is corrected by a change in the structure of the gene, then the NOME provides for the manufacture of certain complex molecules, the insertion of these molecules into the proper receptor neurons in the eyes, and it endows the mind with the ability to experience color when these neurons send ionic impulses to the brain.

Any given electron may respond to electrical and gravitational fields coming from the far reaches of the universe. The associated NOMEs appear to be cosmic in extension.

Morphogenetic Fields

A theory involving nonmaterial essences, which Rupert Sheldrake calls "morphogenetic fields," is proposed by him in his book "A New Science of Life." He writes that

> the existing theories of physics may well be incapable of explaining the unique structure of complex molecules and crystals; they permit a range of possible minimum-energy structures to be

suggested, but there is no evidence that they can account for the fact that one rather than another of these possible structures is realized. . . . The hypothesis that will now be developed is based on the idea that this "selection" is brought about by a new type of causation, at present unrecognized by physics, through the agency of morphogenetic fields.

. . . although morphogenetic fields can only bring about their effects in conjunction with energetic processes, they are not in themselves energetic.[4]

Sheldrake further suggests, as one possibility, that the first molecular structure involving a given set of atoms attained a special low energy configuration by the accidental encounter of these atoms. Once this molecule is formed it sets up an associated morphogenetic field, which is spaceless and timeless, and which guides other similar assemblies of atoms, wherever they may occur, into the same molecular configuration. Each of these new molecules contributes to the strength of the associated morphogenetic field.

When several molecules of various types set up a special structure, this structure establishes a morphogenetic field, which is one step higher in the hierarchy of such fields, and which can influence the fields below it in the hierarchal structure. As the complexity of the physical structure grows, so also grows this pyramid of morphogenetic fields. This process of developing a pyramid of morphogenetic fields is assumed, by Sheldrake, to extend to biological structures. In humans conscious experience is a function of the highest level in the hierarchy of morphogenetic fields. Consciousness exerts its will on the brain and body through its influence on the fields in the lower levels of the associated hierarchy of fields.

In a subsequent book titled *The Presence of the Past: Morphic Resonance and the Habits of Nature,* Sheldrake enlarges on the properties of morphogenetic fields (which he also calls morphic fields). Sheldrake holds that in addition to its structure-molding capabilities, the morphogenetic field of an animal, rather than its genetic molecule, is the home of the memory of the habits of the associated species and influences the animal to perform in accordance with these habits. According to Sheldrake,

> as a swallow grows up, it flies, feeds, preens, migrates, mates, and nests as swallows habitually do. It inherits the instincts of its species through invisible influences, acting at a distance, that make the behavior of past swallows in some sense present within it. It draws on and is shaped by the collective memory of its species.[5]

He suggests that in humans memories may be stored in morphogenetic fields. "Our memories may not be stored inside our brains as we usually assume they may be."[6] To support his theory that memory does not reside in the structure of the brain, Sheldrake needs to explain why removal of or damage to special areas of the brain is found to cause loss of memory. For example, Gardner says: "Bilateral removal of the hippocampi causes global amnesia."[7]

Sheldrake speculates that the laws of nature are not eternal, but possibly they evolved as the material things of nature evolved:

> If the evolving regularities of nature are not governed by transcendent laws, could they not be more like habits? . . . Habits develop within nature; they are not imposed on the world ready made. . . . This general possibility—the possibility that the regularities of nature are more like habits than products of transcendent laws—is what this book explores.[8]

I believe that the NOMEs in nature preceded and molded the objects of nature from the fundamental particles. The laws of nature, usually expressed in mathematical terms, are artifacts conceived by scientists to help them predict how material things move and change. These laws evolve as more subtle measurements made by scientists reveal new aspects of nature. But these manmade laws should not be confused with the NOMEs which implement nature's processes.

Sheldrake supports his theories concerning morphogenetic fields by observations on the habits of things in nature.

> The best-documented example of the spontaneous spread of a new habit concerns the opening of milk bottles by birds. They open the caps on bottles delivered to doorsteps early in the morning and drink as much as two inches of milk from the bottles. . . .
>
> The first record of this habit was from Southampton in 1921, and its spread was recorded in intervals from 1930 to 1947. It has been observed in eleven species, but most frequently in . . . blue tits.
>
> Tits do not usually venture more than a few miles from their breeding place. . . . Hence new appearance of the habit more than fifteen miles from where it had previously been recorded probably represents new discoveries by individual birds. . . . It was independently discovered by individual tits at least 89 times in the British Isles.
>
> The habit also appeared in Sweden, Denmark, and Holland.[9]

The implication that Sheldrake draws from this evidence is that the propensity for the habit spread from the Southampton tits to the tits at the other locations occurred through the associated morphogenetic field. Possibly, however, the tits at the other locations, being as smart as the Southampton tits, may have discovered the milk stealing technique on their own initiative.

Events of the cited type are not conclusive evidence of the reality of morphogenetic fields. Direct evidence of the presence of these fields has not yet been obtained. Until some direct indication of the presence of a morphogenetic field is observed, it must be viewed as a highly speculative concept.

The Body as a Matter-Energy System

The human body is composed of many billions of atoms of various kinds in very complex configurations. The nucleus of any given atom contains over 99.97 percent of the mass of the atom; the remainder of the mass, less than .03 percent, is contained in the electrons of the atom. If the size of the nucleus of an atom in the body were increased to that of a golf ball, then, to the same scale, the distance in any direction to the next atomic nucleus would be a quarter of a mile. The total volume of all the nuclei and all the electrons of all the atoms in the body is equal to one-trillionth of the volume of the body.

The bulk of the body is occupied by the electric field. The electric field holds the atoms in their positions in the structure of the body, and mediates most of the body's processes. Thus volumetrically and operationally the body is essentially an electric field.

When you press your finger against your forehead you feel a hard smooth surface. There is no actual contact between the atoms of the finger and the atoms of the forehead. And in spite of the large distances between adjacent atomic nuclei in both the finger and the forehead, penetration of the atoms of the finger and the forehead into each other's space is prevented by their respective electric fields. It is this NOME (represented by the electric field and the associated laws) that provides the finger with the illusion that it has encountered a smooth, hard surface. Consequently the body must be viewed as consisting of matter and a NOME represented in science as an electric field and its associated mathematical equations.

The mind is also a NOME. The interactions between mental events and behavior of the body are open to introspective observation. I will attempt to follow the scientific procedure in discussing the subject of mind by specifying a mental energy and by exploring laws relating to the interactions between the mental and physical events, some of which can be stated in mathematical terms. Again it is emphasized that the energy and the equations are not the NOME. They are, as in physical science, useful surrogates for the NOME. The nature of the NOME, the manner in which it contains its laws and implements their effects on material things remains a mystery.

Part Three

The Brain

Chapter Seven

Neural Structure and Processes

The Neuron

The sensing, transmission, and processing of information, and the transmission of control signals in a person's body are performed by the brain (the central nervous system) and the peripheral nervous systems that connect the various parts of the body to the brain.

The basic operational element in all these nervous systems is the nerve cell called the *neuron*. The neuron is so constructed that when it is properly stimulated at its input terminals it transmits electrical impulses to its output terminals where they may excite the input terminals of other neurons. The functions performed by the peripheral nervous systems and the brain depend on how these neurons are structured and interconnected.

Although much has been learned about the neuron, scientific insight into this very complex nerve element is still considered by neuroscientists to be embryonic. I will select out of the literature those aspects of the neuron that bear on the subject of this book, and I will treat them in a simplified manner, omitting details that are not pertinent to this discourse.[1]

The Neuron Structure

The neuron is a single cell structure. The heart of the neuron is the cell body. It contains the nucleus of the neuron and the biochemical mechanism for making many of the substances needed to support the processes in the neuron.

Attached to the cell body are filaments, called dendrites, through which impulses, coming from other neurons, may be transmitted to the cell body.

Leading away from the cell body is a tubelike structure called an axon which conducts impulses away from the cell body. At its terminus, the axon separates into a large number of filaments called telodendria through which flow the impulses being delivered by the axon.

A telodendrium of a given neuron can transmit impulses to a dendrite of another neuron with which it is in close proximity. The junction between a dendrite and a telodendrium across which the impulse passes from one neuron to the next is called a synapse, and the gap between the surfaces of the telodendrium and the dendrite across which the impulse is transmitted is called the synaptic cleft. The distance across the synaptic cleft between the two surfaces is 200 to 300 Angstroms.* Synaptic junctions for the cross-neural transmission of signals can also exist between an axon and a dendrite, an axon and an axon, and an axon and a cell body.

A neuron in the peripheral nervous system typically has only a few synaptic junctions with other neurons. A neuron in the central nervous system, the brain, may have 1,000 to 10,000 synaptic junctions with other neurons and it may receive inputs from as many as a thousand other neurons.

A thin membrane constitutes the outer skin of the neuron. It contains complex molecular systems whereby the flows of ions into and out of the neuron are controlled.

Additional aspects of the structure of the neuron will be introduced later at appropriate points in the discussion of the neuronal processes.

---

* An Angstrom is one ten-millionth of a millimeter.

The Ions in and around a Neuron

There are ions of several substances in and around each neuron, the movements of which mediate the flow of electrical impulses through the neuron. The principal actors that will feature in the present discussion are positive ions of sodium and potassium.

The "resting" condition of a neuron refers to the condition in which no impulses are moving through the neuron. During the resting condition the concentration of sodium ions is much higher outside the neuron than inside. The reverse is true for the potassium ions. The distribution of ions is such that there exists in the resting condition a positive electric potential difference of 70 millivolts between the outside and the inside of the neuron. This condition is like having a 70 millivolt battery with its positive terminal connected to the outside of the neuron and its negative terminal connected to the inside.

This concentration distribution represents a nonequilibrium condition in the sense that, if the ions were free to move, they would move in a way to eliminate the voltage difference and concentration differences.

The concentration distribution in the resting condition is maintained by the surface membrane of the neuron. The surface membrane contains pumping molecules that remove sodium ions from the interior to the exterior of the neuron, and potassium ions from the exterior to the interior toward achieving the desired nonequilibrium concentrations.

Also distributed along the surface membrane of the neuron are molecular gates, some of which allow the passage of sodium ions, and others the passage of potassium ions when they are properly stimulated by the electric field associated with impulse transmission (as will be described later). The surface membrane is slightly permeable to potassium ions even when the potassium ion gates are closed.

Impulse Transmission

When the dendrites, which are attached to the input end of a given neuron, are impacted at their synapses with other neurons by a chemical transmitter like acetylcholine (released by these other neurons), molecular gates in the surfaces of the dendrites open momentarily (for approximately one millisecond), and allow sodium ions to enter the dendrites. The entrance of sodium ions into the input end of the neuron causes an increase in the electrical potential in that region, and hence a decrease in electrical potential difference between the inside and the outside of the neuron. If sufficient sodium ions enter the neuron in an appropriately brief period of time (by the nearly simultaneous activation of a number of its synapses and/or the very rapid repeated activation of one of its synapses) to cause the electrical potential to exceed a threshold value, called the activation potential, then the electrical potential spike that is established tends to move through the axon of that neuron toward its discharge end.

The contributions of the various dendrites to the buildup of the activation potential are assembled at the cell body. The cell body contains on its surface a large number of synapses with other neurons some of which make positive (excitatory) contributions to the buildup of the activation potential, and some make negative contributions inhibitory to this buildup. The synapses that make negative contributions contain molecular gates which when opened allow the outflow of positive potassium ions or the inflow of negative chlorine ions both of which would counter the effect of the inflow of the positive sodium ions. The neurons that impose these negative contributions on the receptor neuron employ as neurotransmitters amines such as glycine and gamma-amino-butyric acid (GABA) to open the molecular gates in the inhibitory synapses.* As the activation potential builds up, the net potential for driving these inhibitory ion flows

* A given neuron employs as its neurotransmitter only one chemical.

also increases. Thus the buildup of the activation potential necessary to initiate the movement of the electrical potential spike through the axon is, particularly in cerebral neurons, a complex process involving excitatory and inhibitory contributions from many neurons.

The movement of the positive potential spike in the axon is implemented by a complex mechanism. The electric field associated with this initiating slug of positive sodium ions opens voltage activated molecular gates in the surface membrane of the axon directly downstream of the slug, which admit additional sodium ions to the leading edge of the slug and thereby cause a forward movement of the positive electric field. This process continues with the electric field at the leading edge of the slug continuously moving forward, opening new gates for the entrance of sodium ions, until the leading edge of the sodium slug and its positive potential field arrive at the downstream end of the neuron. At the same time, molecular gates and pumps in the surface membrane are at work restoring the original ionic state at the trailing edge of the sodium slug, so that the sodium slug, in its virtual movement down the axon, occupies, at any instant, only a small part of the length of the axon.

The restoring action at the trailing edge of the sodium slug (which also contains some potassium ions) occurs as a result of two processes. First, gates in the surface membrane at the trailing edge of the slug open to allow the outflow of potassium ions which causes a momentary drop of the potential at this edge even below the resting potential. Then there is a restoration of the resting potential and the ionic composition within the neuron through the action of the pumping gates, readying the neuron for the next activation impulse.

It should be noted that this process of moving the potential spike, by continuously injecting sodium ions into the leading edge of the ionic slug, provides an electric current and an associated potential spike which are independent of the length of the axon. In contrast, the electric current in a wire, with a given potential difference between the input and output ends, depends on the length of the wire; the longer the wire the smaller is the current.

Axons in the human body range in length from as much as three feet (in the peripheral nervous system) to a small fraction of an inch (as found in the brain) and nature has provided this extremely ingenious system for surmounting the variable resistance problem posed by this variation in axon length.

The Influence of the Myelin Layer on Pulse Speed

Some neurons are provided with a myelin layer. This layer is a thin sheath that surrounds the axon and insulates it from the fluid outside the neuron. At more or less regular intervals along the axon there are short circumferential gaps in the myelin layer (called nodes of Ranvier) where the axon is again exposed to contact with the external fluid.

When a sodium ion spike is established in the inlet end of a neuron, the electric current caused by the advent of this spike must go through the first node of Ranvier downstream of the spike where the axon is not insulated and it causes the electrically controlled molecular gates to open and admit sodium ions, establishing a new spike at this position along the axon. This process continues, and provides in effect, a jumping of the neural impulse along the axon from one node of Ranvier to the next. By this process a large increase in speed of transmission of neural impulses in axons is achieved relative to the speed in axons of unmyelinated neurons.

The impulse transmission speed in axons also depends on the diameter of the axon. The impulse transmission speed ranges from 120 meters per second for large diameter (20 micrometer) myelinated axons to one meter per second for small diameter (1 micrometer) unmyelinated axons.[2]

The myelin layer terminates at the end of the axon; it does not cover the other portions of the neuron. The brain contains small diameter neurons, some of which are myelinated and others are not. The white portions of the brain contain for the most part myelinated axons; the gray portions are occupied mainly by cell bodies and unmyelinated neurons.

The number of impulses that pass through a given neuron per second depends on the intensity of the excitation at its input end and can vary from one impulse per second for a weak excitation to 300 pulses per second for a strong excitation. One neural pulse is very much like another, so that an individual pulse, per se, conveys no contextual information.

Elements of contextual information, such as represented by the viewing of the letter A, are encoded as special sequences of neural pulses in the neurons involved in the transmission of this information to the brain. The mental experiences evoked by the neural inputs to the brain depend both on the location of the neural assembly in the brain that is activated by the inputs and the neural pulse sequences.

Transmission of Signals Across Synaptic Gaps

The transmission of impulses from one neuron to the next across the synaptic gaps is implemented mainly by a class of substances called chemical transmitters. A chemical transmitter that features largely in interneural transmission is acetylcholine. Some other chemical transmitters are norepinephrine, gamma-amino-butyric acid, serotonin, dopamines, and histamine. Additional chemical transmitters are continuously being discovered. The following discussion, centered on acetylcholine, illustrates some of the processes involved in interneuron signal transmission.

The chemical transmitter acetylcholine is manufactured in the cell body of the neuron and is loaded into tiny capsules called vesicles. The vesicles flow downstream in the axon of the neuron (pushed along by special molecules in the axon) and assemble in the vicinity of the output synapses. When a pulse of positive sodium ions arrives at the downstream end of the neuron, it interacts with the vesicles to initiate the following sequence of processes:

1. A number of vesicles are caused, each to merge with the surface membrane of the neuron in the vicinity of a synapse.

2. An orifice then forms in each of these merged sections of surface through which the content of the vesicle is discharged into the synaptic cleft.

3. The orifice closes.

4. Each vesicle disengages from the neuron surface membrane and flows back to the cell body for a refill of acetylcholine.

Each vesicle releases about 10,000 molecules of acetylcholine, which cross the synaptic cleft in less than 0.1 milliseconds and open 2,000 gates in the surface membrane of the postsynaptic neuron. The number of vesicles that discharge per neural pulse seems to be controlled by the concentration of calcium ions within the neuron in the discharge zone. More will be said about the function of the calcium ions later.

When the acetylcholine discharged by one neuron crosses the synaptic cleft and impacts on the surface of the adjacent neuron, it produces two effects. First, it causes molecular gates to open in this second neuron which allow the entry of sodium ions into this neuron that contribute to the buildup of the activation potential. Second, it causes the release of a chemical from that surface which destroys the acetylcholine thereby limiting its effective duration and restoring the condition in the synaptic cleft in preparation for the transmission of the next signal.

A similar sequence of events occurs with other neurotransmitters. A given neuron discharges only one kind of neurotransmitter. Some neurons make a contributory input to the buildup of the activation potential in the receptor neuron and others make an inhibitory input. Thus whether a given neuron in the brain fires depends on the net input from many other neurons.

The foregoing description of the signal transmission in neurons is an extremely simplified version of the actual process. One marvels at nature's ingenuity in providing the complex chemicals, structures, and processes needed to achieve an operational system. While the slow signal transmission speed of unmyelinated neurons was adequate for early small living species, it was essential for nature to introduce myelination to evolve the larger, more complex species.

The Role of the Calcium Ion in Signal Modulation

A neuron X may have synapses located near its terminal section where chemical transmitters released by other neurons may mediate an increase in calcium ion flow into neuron X. The increased calcium ion concentration at the terminal section of neuron X increases the number of vesicles of chemical transmitter discharged by neuron X per neural impulse arriving at its terminal section. Thus the intensity of the output of any given neuron per neural impulse passing through it can be modulated by the control of calcium ion concentration at its terminal end by processes in other neurons. In this manner a special sequence of impulses representing a particular item of information may be amplified without disturbing the sequence.[3]

Receptor, Afferent, and Efferent Neurons

Receptor neurons that initially introduce into the nervous systems signals from the environment and from the body are provided at their input ends with special structures adapted to the modality of these signals. The skin, for example, contains several kinds of receptor cells. These cells, when properly stimulated at some point on the skin, can, through their neural networks, induce in the mind the sensations of touch, pressure, pain, heat, cold, hair movement, and so forth, and also the impression that these sensations are occurring at the stimulated point on the skin. Receptor cells for the auditory system are located in the inner ear and are structured to be activated by the movement of hairs that are in contact with them. These hairs are supported and moved by a membrane that is vibrated by a connecting system when air waves vibrate the ear drum. The nerves on the retina of the eye contains special chemicals that are dissociated by the light focused on the retina, thereby initiating the signal pulse. Nerves in the nose and on the tongue contain special chemicals that react with the molecules impinging on these organs to initiate the associated signal pulses.

The receptor neurons, and the neurons that connect the receptor neurons to the brain, that is, all the neurons that transmit sensory signals, are called afferent neurons. The neurons that transmit control signals, for example, from the brain to the muscles of the body are called efferent neurons. In reflex systems the afferent neurons are connected directly through synapses to the efferent neurons in order to reduce response time. The nerve system that causes blinking of the eyes, when they suddenly detect the approach of a fast-moving object, is an example of a reflex system.

An efferent neuron causes muscular response by releasing a chemical transmitter (e.g., acetylcholine) at its synapses with the muscular fibers when neural pulses arrive at these synapses. Some neurons release a chemical transmitter that tenses the muscle; other neurons release a chemical transmitter that relaxes the muscle. The flexing of the arm at the elbow is caused by the tensing of the biceps, and the straightening of the arm is caused by the tensing of the triceps. When the biceps are tensed, the triceps must be relaxed, and vice versa. Otherwise a muscular spasm would result from the conflict between these two opposing sets of muscles.

The Saccharides

Attached to the outer surface of the neuron is a light fuzzlike structure made up of substances called saccharides. These saccharides contain positively and negatively charged sites that attract and bind ions found outside the neuron.

Concentrations of saccharides are found around synaptic junctions, the region where the axon joins the cell body, and the nodes in the myelin layers that surround the neuron. These sites are involved in the excitation and movement of ionic impulses in the neuron. Changes in the ionic affinity in the saccharides in these sites may influence the neural impulse transmission process.

It has been demonstrated experimentally that the electrical state outside the neurons change with learning. This finding has led to the suggestion that changes in saccharide configuration and charge distribution may be involved in information storage and retrieval.[4]

Electrical currents are detected in an elaborate network of channels within the saccharide structures. These currents are related to the currents involved in electroencephalographic (EEG) measurements.

The Glial Cells

The glial cells surround and provide structural support for the neurons of the brain. They also support the blood vessels through which nourishment is conveyed to the brain and waste products are removed. The glial cells do not completely fill the space between the neurons. Part of this space is occupied by the saccharides and the metabolic and ionic substances involved in the impulse transmission phenomena in the neurons.

The glial cells exchange proteins with the neurons and contribute to the regulation of the ionic concentrations in and around the neurons.

Chapter Eight

Some Brain Components and Their Functions

The brain is an organ of incredible complexity in structure, process, and function. Concerning the status of scientific inquiry into the brain, the neuroscientist, Eccles writes:

> We are beginning to understand the simpler patterns of the neuronal organization and the way they work. However, we are still at a very early stage of our attempt to understand the brain, which may well be the last of all frontiers of knowledge that man can attempt to penetrate and encompass. I predict that it will occupy hundreds of years into the future.[1]

I will not attempt, nor is it within my capability, to provide a detailed review of the current information on the brain. I will limit my description of the brain to those items that will be involved in the subsequent discussion of the relation between brain processes and mental processes. Although future research will provide considerably more insight into the brain processes it will, in all likelihood, not illuminate the central mystery, namely, the bridge between the brain processes and the mental processes. This bridge relates to the "hidden transducer" whereby ionic flow patterns in the neural structure of the brain induce conscious experiences. I believe, therefore, that the present understanding of the brain processes suffices for a philosophical discussion of the brain-mind relations.

Mapping the Brain Functions

Major contributions to mapping the human brain with regard to function were made by Penfield and his associates at the Montreal Neurological Institute. This research was accomplished as an adjunct to brain surgery on 1,132 patients troubled with epilepsy, tumors, and other brain problems.

The brain is devoid of pain-sensing receptors. Brain surgery, therefore, can be performed with only a local anesthetic applied to the scalp. Part of the scalp and skull are removed, and the patient, with his brain exposed, is able to converse with the surgeon.

The surgeon uses as his exploratory probe an extremely fine needle attached to a source of electricity. The surgeon inserts the probe at a point in the brain, switches on the electricity (approximately 2 or 3 volts) and observes the patient's response. The response may be the clutching of the right hand or a movement of the left foot or a statement by the patient that he has experienced a flash of light or a buzzing noise or has recalled some past, forgotten event.

The General Configuration of the Brain

The complexity of the human brain in structure and process may be appreciated from the facts that the brain contains approximately 100 billion neurons and that a neuron may have from 1,000 to 10,000 synapses and may receive inputs from as many as 1,000 other neurons. The brain weighs between 1,200 and 1,500 grams. Among humans no correlation has been found between brain weight and mental capability. Einstein, for example, possessed a brain of average weight.

In connection with the presentation of his concept of mind, Penfield identifies three major areas of the brain: the lower brain stem, the upper brain stem, and the cerebral cortex. The lower brain stem is connected at its base to the spinal cord and leads into the upper brain stem which is a much more elaborate neural structure. The upper brain stem contains among other systems a very complex neural structure called the diencephalon located at its upper end. The cerebral cortex lies above the higher brain stem and extends down and around it like a large highly convoluted cap. The cerebral cortex includes the neocortex (the new brain), the hippocampus, and some elements of the olfactory system.

Paul MacLean in his concept of the triune brain[2] also divides the brain into three zones; but the boundaries of these zones differ from those specified by Penfield. MacLean's categorization follows what he considers to be contributions from the various stages in the evolutionary history of *Homo sapiens*. A segment that includes the lower brain stem and small special portions of the higher brain stem and cortex is, MacLean believes, a contribution of man's reptilian ancestry; he labels it the reptilian complex. The remainder of the higher brain stem and additional portions of the cerebral cortex which developed during the early mammalian period in man's evolution he labels the limbic system. The neocortex, the third segment in MacLean's categorization, had its major development during the later mammalian period. As evolution progressed the configuration and functions of these three portions of the brain, of course, changed. Nonetheless MacLean speculates that the reptilian portion is strongly involved in a person's aggressive and ritualistic behavior, that more subtle states of mind such as moods, emotions, and altruistic and religious feelings are related strongly to the limbic system, and that reasoning is a function of the neocortex. Carl Sagan elaborates on this theme in his book *The Dragons of Eden*.[3]

The sharp partition of function among the components of the brain is of course a gross oversimplification. A person's behavior is largely orchestrated by the brain as a whole. This point will be developed as the discussion proceeds.

Although man's capability for such exotic performance as abstract reasoning stems from his highly developed neocortex, nevertheless, according to Penfield, consciousness appears to be related to activity in the diencephalon in the upper brain stem.[4] Thatcher and John[5] associate consciousness with activity in a broader region, largely in the brain stem, which includes the diencephalon, the reticular formation (a complex of neurons that runs longitudinally along the midline of the brain stem), and some part of the neocortex adjacent to the brain stem.

The Brain Stem

The nerves connecting to the various peripheral areas of the body enter the cranium through the spinal cord and feed into the brain stem. The brain stem is somewhat larger in diameter than the spinal cord at their junction and expands in diameter as it approaches the neocortex. The diencephalon, the uppermost portion of the brain stem, includes the thalamus and the hypothalamus. The reticular formation runs up through the midline of the brain stem from the lower brain stem into the diencephalon.

The brain stem contains other neural assemblies essential to the operation of the brain but which do not figure in the subsequent discussion and are therefore not introduced here.

Attached to the rear of the brain stem near its top just under the neocortex lies the cerebellum. The cerebellum is a very large assembly of neurons that become involved in the precise control of bodily movements. At the front of the brain stem also near the top just under the neocortex are two olfactory lobes, small neural ensembles that receive inputs from the olfactory receptors located in the membrane of the nasal cavity, and that transmit to the olfactory cortex in the upper brain stem. Also just under the neocortex is a neural structure called the hippocampus. The olfactory lobes and cortex and the hippocampus are part of the cerebral cortex.

The Neocortex

The neocortex, the latest contribution to the brain in the evolutionary process, is present not only in humans but also in other mammals, such as the whale, the dolphin, the cat, the dog, the primates, and the like. The neocortex in the human species reached its present size and configuration over 40,000 years ago with the development of the prefrontal and temporal lobes, presaging the advent of *Homo sapiens.*

The human neocortex is a 0.1 inch (2 mm) thick sheet of neurons, which, if it were spread flat, would cover an area equal to 1.5 square feet. *In situ* within the cranium the neo-cortex is convoluted to form a layer 6 inches thick. The neocortex constitutes 75 percent of the weight of the brain. With this large neocortex man was able to develop his re-markable mental capabilities.

A segment of the neocortex running laterally across the top and part way down the sides, half way between the front and rear of the brain, is the motor cortex. The various muscles that move the components of the body are activated by neurons in the motor cortex. The neurons at the top center control the toes, and as one progresses away from the center toward the sides and bottom, one locates the other functions, for example, the knees, hip, trunk, and so on, until one even-tually arrives at the face, lips, tongue, and swallowing motor nerves at the bottom of the motor cortex. The right and left segments of the motor cortex are mirror images with regard to location of function. The right half of the motor cortex activates the muscles in the left side of the body, and the left half activates muscles in the right side of the body.

Just behind the motor cortex, and parallel to it, lies the somatic sensory cortex. The somatic sensory cortex receives sensory signals from the peripheral structure of the body. The mapping of the human anatomy on the somatic sensory cor-tex nearly parallels that on the motor cortex.[6] The somatic sensory cortex and the motor cortex cooperate in the activa-tion and control of the peripheral muscles.

The motor and somatic sensory cortices should be viewed, not as the total control of the muscular movement, but rather as major relay areas. The muscular control efforts are aided by the cerebellum composed of an enormous number of neurons* with afferent and efferent neural connections with the motor and somatic sensory cortices. The cerebellum cooperates with these other cortices in a feedback type process to fine tune the control of the muscular movement. The cerebellum, for example, makes possible the precise control of muscular movements involved in the playing of a musical instrument. The cerebellum is not part of the neocortex; it lies behind the upper part of the brain stem just under the rearward portion of the neocortex.

The prefrontal lobe, located at the front of the neocortex, and the temporal lobes, located near the bottom of the right and left sides of the neocortex, are the latest development of the neocortex. Among other functions, these additions provide for storage and recall of past experiences. These lobes are absent in the brains of lesser animals and are major contributors to the superior reasoning capability of *Homo sapiens*. The hippocampus, located under each temporal lobe, is also involved in memory storage and recall. The actual sites of the memory storage may be in the cerebellum and various other portions of the cortex.

The Wernicke and Broca areas are major elements in language management. The Wernicke area arranges words in grammatical sequence to form meaningful statements. Damage to the Wernicke area can cause loss of ability to understand written and spoken language. The Broca area is connected to the Wernicke area by a major nerve system and it feeds information received from the Wernicke area into the motor cortex to activate the muscles involved in speech. For right-handed people, the Broca area is located on the left side of the neocortex just ahead of the motor cortex and adjacent to the section that controls the muscles of the speaking apparatus. The Wernicke area is located near the Broca area but just behind the somatic sensory cortex. Other cortices can

---

* The cerebellum contains 30,000 million granule cells, 30 million Purkinje cells, and 200 million basket and stellate cells.

make inputs to the Wernicke area. What one sees, hears, smells, thinks, and so forth, may influence what one says or writes.

The primary auditory cortex is in the temporal lobe just below the Wernicke area. It receives and processes information from the auditory system. After being processed through the complex of auditory cortices, the information is transmitted to the Wernicke area where understanding of the spoken sentences is implemented.

The neocortex is divided along a line running from the front to the rear into two nearly equal parts called the right and left hemispheres. The left hemisphere controls the movements of the right side of the body; the right hemisphere controls the movements of the left side of the body. The two hemispheres are connected for two-way communication and cooperation by a bundle of nerves called the *corpus callosum,* that consists of 200 million neurons.

At the rear of each hemisphere is a visual cortex. Information from the right visual fields of both eyes is transmitted to the visual cortex in the left hemisphere; the left visual fields record in the visual cortex in the right hemisphere.

Because of the location of the Broca and Wernicke areas in the left hemisphere, this hemisphere handles ideation in thought, speech, and writing; it is the logical side of the brain. The right hemisphere is the intuitive side. It specializes in such areas as art, music, and nonverbal ideation. Both hemispheres cooperate in, for example, an attempt to conceive a new scientific theory where both logic and intuition are involved.

In a very small percentage of left-handed people, the Broca and Wernicke areas are in the right hemisphere with the result that the specializations of the hemispheres noted in the previous paragraph are reversed. Furthermore, it is found that there is not a sharp cleavage in function between the hemispheres, but that each hemisphere has some vestige of the other hemisphere's capabilities.[7, 8, 9]

Nerve bundles in the neocortex called association cortices interconnect various of the other cortices and assist in mediating their interactions. A more detailed description of the visual and auditory systems will be given in chapter 9, and the specializations of the two hemispheres will be discussed in chapter 10.

The Control Function of the Brain Stem

Although the neocortex appears to handle the most advanced processes of the brain, it now is believed that the main seat of control is in the brain stem. Penfield points out:

> Recent studies show that each sensory input, whether auditory or visual, or from the great somatic sensory systems of the body, gives off collateral branches on its way to the thalamus, the uppermost nucleus in the brain stem. These collaterals feed into the reticular formation of the brain stem. This may well give the reticular formation a means of inhibiting or reinforcing incoming sensory messages in relation to the thalamic or cortical reception of these messages.[10]

> There is much evidence of a level of integration within the central nervous system that is (functionally) higher than that to be found in the cerebral cortex, evidence of a regional localization of the neuronal mechanism involved in integration. I suggest that this region lies not in the new brain (the cortex) but in the old (the brain stem).[11]

Thatcher and John in addressing the same subject say:

> The thalamus, which in humans is about the size of a closed fist, occupies the very middle of the head. Nearly all sensory input interact directly or indirectly with neurons in the thalamus. The thalamus has been likened to a "Grand Central Station," carrying out the switching or "gating" of peripheral sensory drives to specific cortical regions as well as integrating sensory-motor outflow activities.[12]

It is these centers (thalamus and reticular formation) that are involved in the control of arousal and attention, the production of alpha rhythms and related EEG phenomena, the initiation of the orienting reflex and the creation of representational systems, recall from memory, the integration of electrically pulsed information, and it is these midline systems that make fundamental contributions to the maintenance of consciousness and sensory awareness.[13]

Chapter Nine

On Sensory Inputs to the Brain

The Visual System

It is believed that the neurons in the retina of the eye, on which the visual image is focused, were once part of the cerebral system in man's early progenitors and were extruded into their present position in the course of the evolutionary process. This extrusion is noted during the development of a human fetus into a mature embryo.

The eyeball is a spherical shell about one inch in diameter which contains a lens system for focusing images on the retina (a complex of neurons and blood vessels disposed on the surface of the eyeball behind the lens system). The lens system consists of a fixed lens, the cornea, at the front of the eyeball, which focuses objects in the distance range from infinity to twenty feet from the observer, and an adjustable lens located slightly behind the cornea that assists in focusing closer objects. The shape of the adjustable lens is controlled by a set of muscles in the eyeball.

The retina contains three layers of neural cells. The outermost layer, on which the image falls, is composed of receptor cells. Behind this layer is a layer of neurons, called bipolar cells, each of which synapses with several of the receptor cells. And finally there is a layer of neurons, called ganglion cells, each of which synapses with a number of the bipolar cells. The axons of the ganglion cells gather together in a bundle to form the optic nerve. The optic nerve emerges from the eyeball through a small area at its rear. Thus there is some processing of the visual signals before the optic nerve leaves the eyeball.

The receptor neurons are of two kinds, rods and cones, so named because of the shapes of their receptor segments. The receptor segments are attached to cell bodies which then project signals from the receptor segments to their synapses. Each receptor segment contains a number of parallel plates on which are disposed photo-sensitive chemicals. The rods all contain the same chemical (rhodopsin). Each cone in a color-sensitive person contains one of three different chemicals. The chemical in the rods and cones, when struck by photons of light, ionize and initiate neural impulses that, on traversing the neural pathways to the brain, evoke mental experiences of light. A cone generates a sensation of red, green, or blue depending on the kind of chemical its receptor segment contains. The light wavelengths that activate these chemicals are 450um for blue, 535um for green, and 600um for red (one um = one millionth of a meter).

There are approximately six million cones and thirty million rods. A very small, especially sensitive area in the center of the retina, the fovea, contains exclusively cones. As one proceeds away from the fovea toward the periphery of the retina one encounters a mixture of cones and rods, with the percentage of cones decreasing as the periphery is approached. Within the retina are blood vessels that service the neurons, and glial cells that support the blood vessels and neurons.

After the optic nerves leave the two eyeballs, they come together at a region called the optic chiasm where the axons that transmit information from the left sides of the visual fields of both eyes gather and proceed to the primary zone of the visual cortex in the right hemisphere of the brain. On the way to the visual cortex these optic nerves synapse with neurons in the thalamus (in the brain stem). The axons that transmit information from the right sides of visual fields of both eyes follow a similar path but terminate in the primary zone of the visual cortex in the left hemisphere. The corpus callosum mediates the joining of the right and left portions of the visual field into a complete picture.

The primary zones of the visual cortices are each blocked off into units having a length and a width of approximately 1 mm and the full thickness of the cortex, namely 2 mm. Each of these one square millimeter units is associated with specific incremental areas in the retinas of both eyes. Thus there is a systematic projection of areas in the retina onto areas in the cortex. A similar correspondence occurs between areas in the retina and the thalamus.

I will touch on a few features of the very complex structure of the primary visual cortex. This cortex consists of six layers disposed parallel to its surface. Each square millimeter unit of the cortex may be viewed as containing a number of zones parallel to one another and running at right angles to the surface of the cortex through the six neural layers. The neurons in all the layers of a given zone (except for layer four) fire when the image of a line or an edge of a given angle strikes the increment of retinal surface to which this cortical unit relates. As the image of a line progressively changes its angle in discrete increments (roughly between 10 and 20 degrees), the neurons in successive zones of the square millimeter unit progressively fire. The neurons in layer four fire for all angles of the line. Signals from both eyes are received in each cortical unit and are processed in a complex manner.

As pointed out in chapter 7, a single neural impulse conveys no substantive information. Information transmittal involves special sequences of impulses and the special portions of the brain that receive these impulses. In the case of the transmission of color information from the cones in the retina to the visual cortex, nothing is known about the sequence of impulses that represent each of the colors or about the neural structures in the cortex that respond to the color signals.

Adjoining the primary visual area are secondary and tertiary visual areas that receive information from the primary area. In the secondary area information on form, color, stereoptic depth, and movement are combined to produce the neural representation of the total visual input. The visual information in the right and left hemispheres are joined through the corpus callosum to integrate the inputs from both sides of the visual field. The tertiary area receives inputs from other sensory cortices and associates them with the visual inputs in the formation of more complex relationships. How the secondary and tertiary areas are structured and perform their various tasks are not yet known.

The secondary and tertiary areas connect to the thalamus through neural systems for two-way communication. Although they are associated with different areas in the thalamus than the primary area, the several areas are interconnected. The visual information is also transmitted to the reticular formation of neurons that runs along the midline of the brain stem. The thalamus and reticular formation are interconnected with other cortices of the brain and serve as general integrative, exchange, and control centers.

A lesion in a person's primary visual area produces a blind spot in his vision. A lesion in the secondary area interferes with the person's ability to perceive an assembly of forms as a total structure. A. R. Luria describes the confused reaction of a patient with such a lesion to the picture of a pair of spectacles. The patient said he saw a circle, another circle, a stick, a crossbar, but he could not identify the assembly as a pair of spectacles. He ventured the opinion that the assembly might be a bicycle.

Massive destruction of the secondary and tertiary areas of the visual cortex render a person blind, even though the primary cortex is intact and its neurons are responding to patterns placed before the person's eyes. Thus it appears that the mental experience of sight is not associated with the neural activity in the primary cortex but rather with activity in areas where greater integration of the neural signals occurs. (See note 1 for references to a more complete discussion of the visual system.)[1]

There is no segment of tissue in the brain on which a graphic image of the scene being viewed by the eyes is projected. There exist in the brain complex sequences of neural impulses. Regarding the representation in the brain of the image of a tree swaying in the breeze, Thatcher and John point out:

> Obviously, the internal representation does not resemble a tree. It is in some other form, most likely involving distributed but coordinated neural activity shifting and swaying in an orderly fashion as the tree sways.[2]

The Auditory System

It is said that the auditory system is the most complex sensory system in the body. I will describe some of the salient features of this system. (I have used some of the works in note 3 for this discussion.)[3]

The auditory structure is divided into three sections, the outer ear, the middle ear, and the inner ear. The outer ear contains a tubular air passage, the ear canal, which is sealed at its inner end by a membrane, the ear drum. Air vibrations impacting on the outer ear pass through the ear canal to the ear drum and cause the ear drum to vibrate in a manner representative of the vibrations in the air.

The middle ear contains three bones (the malleus, the incus, and the stapes) which are so arranged and supported that they may act as a complex lever system for mechanically transmitting the movements of the ear drum to a diaphragm in the inner ear called the oval window.

The oval window resides in the forward face of a helical chamber called the cochlea. As one moves along the cochlea away from the forward face or base, one traces a spiral path having 2 3/4 turns. The distance traversed along this path from the base of the cochlea to its apex is about 35 mm. Two membranes, the basilar membrane and the Reissner membrane, attached to supports that extend from the chamber walls and that follow the spiral path, divide the chamber space into three spiral compartments each of which runs from the base of the cochlea to its apex. These compartments are filled with different liquids.

When the oval window is vibrated, it produces pulses in the liquid in the cochlea with which it is in contact. These pulses course through this liquid and induce vibrations in the basilar membrane. The effective area of the oval window is one-fourteenth that of the ear drum. This fact contributes an amplification factor of 14 to the vibratory pressures in this liquid. In addition the lever system between the ear drum and the oval window contributes an amplification factor of 1.3 with the result that the pressure pulses in the liquid are 18 times greater than the air pressure pulses that impact the ear drum.

The basilar membrane supports along its length a membrane called the organ of Corti, which contains 16,000 receptor cells (neurons without axons) disposed longitudinally in four rows. These cells can, through synapses, introduce impulses into the neural pathways to the brain when their activation potentials are attained. Extending from the upper end of each cell is a clump of about 100 hairs. The longer hairs touch a gelatinous membrane and they are attached by fine filaments to the shorter hairs. When the basilar membrane is vibrated the upper ends of the longer hairs are held in place with the result that the hairs bend. The movement of these hairs mechanically, through the attached filaments, affect the open period of gates at or near the tips of the shorter hairs and permit the flow of positive ions from the surrounding space into the cell. A sufficient influx of positive ions causes the attainment of the activation potential.

The basilar membrane is narrow near the oval window and

gradually widens as it approaches the apex of the cochlea. The basilar membrane in its frequency response is analogous to a xylophone. The narrow section of this membrane, which is the stiffest section, vibrates in resonance with the high frequency vibrations in the cochlear liquid; its resonant frequency gradually decreases as the membrane widens. Thus when a complex vibration consisting of many frequencies is transmitted to the cochlear liquid, different sections of the basilar membrane vibrate, each activating its special neural pathway to the brain.

(The foregoing discussion must be viewed as a broad brush treatment of the structure and processes of the ear. The ear is the most complex sensory organ of the body and is the subject of much continuing research. Research is in progress, for example, to discover a mechanism that may help sharpen the frequency response of the auditory system in order to account for the human capability for fine scale frequency discrimination.)

The neural pathway to the brain is complex and it includes synapses with the thalamus before arriving at the auditory cortex in the neocortex. It appears that at each synaptic junction the spatial xylophone-like distribution of frequency signals, called the tonotopic representation, is preserved.

This tonotopic approach to the transmission of frequency information is necessitated by the fact that the neural system employs pulse frequency to indicate the intensity (loudness in the case of sound) of the signal. Furthermore, pulse sequences are used to transmit contextual information.

The auditory cortex, like the visual cortex, consists of three neuronally connected zones which progressively provide more complex processing of the auditory signals. A lesion in the secondary zone does not interfere with the perception of simple sounds but does interfere with the ability to distinguish complex sound patterns. The tertiary zone handles interactions between auditory and other sensory modalities. These three zones project neural activity back to the thalamus and reticular formation in the brain stem.

It is not yet certain whether the final neural representation of a sound which is transduced into the psychic awareness of a tone occurs in the auditory cortex or in the upper brain stem. This point will be discussed in chapter 13.

It is reasonable to suppose that at each point in the tonotopic organization of the auditory cortex there is a special neuronal microcircuit that builds each special neural representation of pitch. But the nature of this representation is still a mystery.

A note sounded by a given musical instrument consists of vibrations having a fundamental frequency and a series of multiples of this frequency called harmonics. The note is identified by the fundamental frequency; its timbre or tonal quality is determined by the intensities (vibrational amplitudes) of the various harmonics relative to that of the fundamental frequency. The same note on a piano and a violin would have the same fundamental frequency but would differ in the relative intensities of the harmonics.

The mind does not hear the individual harmonics of a given note; it hears the note as a unified entity having a special timbre. The mind has no difficulty distinguishing a given note played on a piano from the same note played on a violin, even when they are played at the same time. In a completely mechanistic concept of mind, in which the mental experience is a passive complementary aspect of a physical representation in the brain, a tone, which is comprised of many harmonics, would have to be associated with a unified representation of the components of the tone.

Interactions among Cortices

The various cortices of the brain are interconnected by nerve systems (e.g., the association cortices, etc.). These interconnections provide complex interactions between the cortices. The Wernicke area through its interconnections with the visual and auditory cortices provides meaning to sentences registered by these cortices. The Wernicke area in association with the cerebral storage bank of words frames replies to these sentences which are fed through the Broca area into the motor cortex to activate the speaking or writing mechanisms of the body. Other cortices come into play in adding emotional overtones to the spoken words.

On Physico-Psychic Transduction

Visual images are transmitted to and processed by the brain as sequences of ionic impulses. Nowhere in the brain are there beams of colored light that translate these ionic impulse sequences into a graphic rendition of the associated image. The lights and the associated picture are purely mental events. There is no light in the physical world as man experiences light.

Similarly, auditory information shows up in the brain as sequences of neural impulses. There are no sounds or words or music, as such, in the brain. These sounds, words, and music are purely mental experiences. Nor is there sound in the physical world; there are instead vibrations.

Neuroscientists have provided no information on the physico-psychic transducer that converts sequences of ionic impulses into mental experiences. Moreover the nature of the transducer in structure and mode of operation would most probably always remain a mystery to the scientist.

G. M. Stratton at the end of the nineteenth century and Wolfgang Kohler in the middle of the twentieth century performed experiments in which the subjects were fitted with lenses of various types that altered their visual inputs. Some of the results of these experiments are summarized by Ragnar Granit. The subjects wore these lenses for a number of days and reported the changes in their visual perceptions with time.

Stratton, using himself as the subject in the experiment, wore lenses that inverted his visual field. At the start of the experiment Stratton saw the room and its contents in the inverted position. After the fifth day of the experiment, Stratton reported that he now perceived that the visual field had reverted to its normal orientation. However, the visual field again appeared inverted after he looked at his body which his mind then used as a reference base. After the eighth day, this reversion did not occur; Stratton felt that he was viewing the scene from an inverted body. Kohler reported substantially similar results from experiments in which he used a number of subjects.

Since the inputs to the neural systems remained basically the same throughout the experiment, the changes in the mind's perception must have resulted from the dynamics of the physico-psychic transducer. The mind knew the field orientation that was proper, and it influenced the physico-psychic transduction process accordingly.

In addition to transducing ionic activity in the visual cortex into mental experiences of light phenomena, and ionic activity in the auditory system into mental experiences of sound, the physico-psychic transducer generates mental experiences of odor from ionic activity in the olfactory system, and it provides a like service for the other sensory modalities. In general, it handles all interactions between the mind and the brain. It is, in essence, the mental NOME.

Chapter Ten

Some Brain System Characteristics

On Information Transmission

A neuron in the brain may connect with the order of 1,000 other neurons. The various cortices of the brain are extensively interconnected. As a result the primary signal being transmitted by a given neuron is submerged in trains of other signals received from connecting neurons. Some of these secondary signals may represent important modifications of the primary signal; other of these inputs may be classified as random noise. It is therefore impossible to distinguish in a given neuron those impulses that are transmitting the primary information.

Nature solves this identification problem by imposing the primary information signal on an ensemble containing many neurons, thereby providing parallel paths for the transmission of this information. The trains of impulses representing the primary signal are in synchronism and therefore their effects are reinforcing. These synchronized impulses build a much more intense representation of the signal than the representation built by impulses in the ensemble that are at random timing with respect to one another. The ultimate representation of the signal conveyed by the ensemble of neurons which generates the mental experiences may be viewed as a large edifice constructed by the synchronized primary impulses, superimposed on which are small perturbations contributed by the random pulses.

If well-synchronized secondary trains of impulses are imposed on the various neurons in the ensemble under discussion by another ensemble of neurons, then this input would have a major effect on the resultant representation provided by this ensemble and would modify the message contained in that representation.

The Orchestrated Dynamics of the Brain

Because of the high degree of interconnection between its neurons, the brain cannot be viewed as a neatly compartmentalized apparatus in which each compartment attends only to its specialization. Instead the brain appears to function as a unified system in which many areas may be involved in the orchestration of a given operation.[1]

Although language processes are mediated largely by the Broca and Wernicke areas, most other areas of the brain are also involved. What one says is stimulated by what one sees, hears, smells, tastes, experiences emotionally, thinks, remembers, and so forth. Damage to other areas of the brain degrade the language processes; the farther toward the front of the brain lies the site of the damage, the more likely is the occurrence of expressive asphasia; the farther toward the rear of the brain the site of the damage, the more likely is the occurrence of receptive language difficulties.[2] Other brain processes also exhibit to a greater or lesser degree dependence on substantial regions of the brain other than the primary mediating cortices.

Even the simple movement of a hand can involve extensive cortical interactions. In addition to the cooperative interplay of the motor and somatic sensory cortices and the cerebellum, the other cortices that mediate the various sensory modalities and the emotions and thoughts can make inputs that can affect the motion of the hand. The hand can react to the sight of an approaching ball, the buzz of a mosquito, and the like. The hand by its movement can indicate supplication, surprise, or despair. The hand guided by the mind can paint a picture, or construct a novel and useful machine, or play a musical composition with much emotional expressiveness.

Functional Pluralism

If a lesion at some site in the brain has impaired a function of the brain by destroying part of the neural organization, the brain, in time, can often provide a new surrogate organization, and thereby restore the impaired function. The location of the new organization need not be precisely at the site where the impaired elements had been located. In fact, it is often found that after restoration of an impaired function, a second lesion, at the same site as the first lesion, does not impair the restored function. Observations by Penfield and others indicate, for example, that Broca's area can be destroyed and the brain can gradually produce a neural organization that provides complete recovery of the speech function.

Thatcher and John, following Ukhtomski, Filimonov, and Luria, points out the "functional pluralism" of the brain's neural organization in the performance of tasks. The desire to perform a given task and the task to be performed may remain constant but the intermediate systems involved can vary substantially.[3] If, for example, a child is restrained from reaching for a piece of candy by blocking the movement of his right hand, his left hand immediately goes into action with the same objective. If a man is prevented from writing a word because his hand had been severed in an accident, he can still write the word, with no physical restructuring of his neural systems by utilizing a pencil grasped within his teeth. The head movements corresponding to the formation of the letters in the word are immediately available to him without any prior training for this operation.

The concept of functional pluralism holds that a given formation of neurons in the brain may become involved in many different functions and in the performance of many tasks.

When the mind sets an objective for the body, many automatic and semiautomatic systems are called into action toward the attainment of the objective. The mind seems to concentrate its attention on the discrepancy between the status of the body and the objective and becomes satisfied when that discrepancy is eliminated. For example, when a man, seated at his desk feels an annoying draft and decides to close the window, his muscles go through a complex series of movements in getting him out of the chair, propelling him toward the window, and closing the window, without any close mental direction of the detailed muscular movements involved. He is merely concerned with where he is with respect to the window and is satisfied when the window is closed. If he should encounter an obstacle, then other systemic operations are brought into play to achieve the closure of the window.

The Attention Process

Attention plays an important role in the neural processes. It has been shown experimentally that the exercise of attention toward some modal signal actually causes an increase in the intensity of the neural processes that transmit this signal.[4]

In 1956, R. Hernandez-Peon et al.[5] recorded the signal from an electrode inserted into the cochlear nucleus of a cat (a region in the brain stem where signals from the ears are processed before being transmitted to the auditory cortex) while the cat was being exposed to a series of clicking sounds, which seemed to have captured its attention. A series of large spikes in the recorded electrical signal were noted, which were in synchronism with the series of clicks, and which were therefore judged to represent the cat's neural response to these clicks. While the clicking continued, a beaker containing some live mice was placed before the cat, diverting its attention. Immediately, the magnitude of the spikes in the signal from the cochlear nucleus decreased very substantially. When the beaker containing the mice was removed, the recorded electrical spikes regained their original amplitudes. The same modulation of recorded spike amplitude was obtained when the cat was exposed to the odor of fish.

Thus the presence or absence of attention actually modulates the intensity of the neural signals. Although it is not known how attention selects and initiates the appropriate neural processes, there appears to be some basis for speculation on how the modal signal modulation might be achieved. It was pointed out in chapter 7 that a neuron may have located at its downstream (output) end input synapses with other neurons where it can receive special chemical transmitters when these other neurons are pulsed. These special chemical transmitters act to modulate the flow of calcium ions in the receptor neuron, which, in turn, controls the number of acetylcholine vesicles that discharge at its synapses per neural pulse transmitted through its axon. The increased flow of acetylcholine at these synapses increases the intensity of the signal input into the postsynaptic neuron.

The absence of attention may account for the decrease in awareness of environmental signals when one is immersed in deep thought, and the decrease in pain intensity when one's interest is otherwise engaged. A sudden sound, sight, or odor signal that may trigger alarm systems in the mind, or a sharp increase in pain, may again direct attention toward and amplify the signal in the neural system involved.

The Memory Process

Memory is a complex process involving possibly three phases. The first is of short duration in which the afferent impulses from a sensory system reverberate through neuronal circuit loops, gradually attenuating until they disappear. This is a short-term memory phase.

If the first phase is of sufficient duration, it allows construction of a biochemical template, which according to Thatcher and John, constitutes an intermediate memory phase that also gradually decays.

The final phase involves the establishment of some irreversible changes in the neural system that provides long-term memory. Old and presumably forgotten items in the long-term memory bank of a person can be retrieved and brought to the person's mind by electrically stimulating a neuron in the temporal lobe.[6]

Neural Changes Associated with Long-Term Memory

It is not yet clear what neural changes are involved in the establishment of long-term memory. Eccles[7] recites experiments by T. V. A. Bliss and T. Lomo[8] in which successive repetitions of a mild stimulus, each of a duration of 20 seconds, generated an increasing intensity of neural response measured in certain neural cells in the hippocampus of the test animal. On the basis of these and similar tests, Eccles postulates that the synapses on spines of the dendrites of certain cerebral neurons (the pyramidal cells of the cerebral cortex and the Purkinje cells of the cerebellum) "are the modifiable synapses concerned in learning." Thus he speculates that memory is encoded by the enhancement of the synaptic structure of a certain set of neurons in the brain. When, in a recall operation, the proper stimulus is introduced into this set, it produces a train of neural responses similar to what occurred with the original sensing of the remembered item and therefore evokes a mental experience similar to the original mental experience. There is, as yet, no direct pictorial evidence (obtained by an electron microscope) of the modification of the synaptic structure of neurons by learning.

On the basis of experiments (by Barondes, Agranoff, and

others) showing that the depression of synthesis of cerebral proteins or RNA inhibits long-term learning, Eccles further suggests that "in the process of learning, neuronal activation leads first to specific RNA synthesis and then in turn to protein synthesis, and so finally to synaptic growth and the coding of the memory."[9]

Obviously some changes in the cerebral structure accompanying learning must occur. Whether it is by the growth of synaptic junctions, as suggested by Eccles, or by the formation of other special structures in or around the neurons, or by the distribution of special molecules, or by combinations of these possibilities is yet to be determined.

On the Memory Engram

Experimentation has shown that a given neuron may be involved in the storage of more than one item of information.[10] The pulse sequence in a single neuron in the brain (as pointed out in the initial section of this chapter) is not definitive of any specific information. Information transmission in the brain is represented by the statistical resultant of trains of impulses in an ensemble comprised of many neurons. Therefore any memory marker, such as an altered synapse condition, set up in any given neuron by its associated impulses can only be considered as one element in a vast ensemble of such markers which constitute the engram for an item of information.

These considerations indicate that a given memory item is not encoded in its own private set of neurons but rather that memory is encoded and recalled by a very complex orchestration of neural events in which many of the same neural elements may be involved in the storage of different items of information.

W. J. Freeman, one of the pioneers in this mass action theory of memory storage and recall, views information processing in terms of the performance of a hierarchy of "K sets" of neurons. In this theory, the elementary information is defined by the neural space-time pattern in the lowest of the K sets, and higher sets are involved in interaction, inhibition, and recall processes.[11]

The Holography Storage of Memory

Pribram suggests that "there need not be only a single memory mechanism" and that "neural modifiability is multifaceted, and memory is not a unitary process."[12] He appears to subscribe to the idea that memory items are encoded by modifications to the spatial pattern of neural junction structure.

Pribram also believes that memory storage and retrieval are mass action processes. He takes as a model the holographic storage of information in solids. He points out that as many as ten billion bits of information have been stored in a cubic centimeter of a solid by the holographic process. Each item of information is stored throughout the solid employing its special spatial-frequency carrier. And it is retrieved by imposing the same spatial-frequency carrier which, by coherently reenforcing the stored pattern, causes it to be revealed. By this means, items are stored and retrieved without the employment of an addressing system. The memory bank in the retrieval process is merely searched by imposing the proper search wave for the desired item.

In Pribram's view, the various memory items are stored in the memory bank of the brain in a manner analogous to the holographic storage in solids. Each item is stored throughout the memory bank of the brain. When a neural wave pattern representing some aspect of a stored item passes through this memory bank, it coherently interacts with the memory markers for the stored item, thereby initiating the neural mass activity that represents the stored item in the purview of the mind.

Although this is an oversimplified and abbreviated description of Pribram's ideas, I believe it captures the gist of his concept. The details of the cerebral process for (a) achieving the holographic distribution of the information, (b) establishing the markers for this information, (c) initiating the appropriate search waves, (d) producing the desired interaction between the search wave and the markers to generate the special neural representation that evokes the subjective experience of the stored information are not understood. The proposed system can only be described in broad conceptual terms.

Pribram's theory that it requires a complex wave of impulses through a bank of neurons to evoke a given memory item seems plausible enough in view of the small significance of a single pulse in a single neuron. But one has difficulty reconciling this theory with Penfield's findings in experiments in which a simple electric pulse into a patient's brain evoked a complex memory train. When, for example, a fine needle, insulated except for the tip, was pressed into the surface of the temporal lobe, and the electric power switched on, the patient is reported to have said:

> Oh! I had the same very, very familiar memory, in an office somewhere. I could see the desks, I was there and someone was calling to me, a man leaning on a desk with a pencil in his hand.[13]

Penfield suggests that the neuronal record was not in the temporal cortex near the point of insertion of the needle but rather in the diencephalon in the area into which the activated neurons in the temporal cortex project impulses.[14] Thatcher and John also point out that experimental results indicate that the "site of stimulation eliciting a response is not necessarily the site of the memory."[15]

Obviously much has yet to be learned about the processes of memory.

On the Role of Attention in Memory

Attention plays a very important role in the first memory phase. It is a common experience for people, after being introduced to a stranger, to immediately forget the stranger's name. However, if one has a special reason for remembering the name of the stranger then one pays attention when the name is stated and the name becomes inscribed in one's long-term memory.

Although the precise neural structure in the brain that mediates this attention control is not yet known, a system may be speculatively conceptualized from known facts about the neurons. To achieve the reverberation capability, the neurons that mediate the first phase of memory may each communicate at its output synapses with auxiliary neurons that either directly, or through connecting neurons, communicate back to input synapses of the initial neuron, thus forming a loop. A pulse in the initial neuron, if it causes a sufficient discharge of chemical transmitter at its synapse with a neuron in the loop, will produce a postsynaptic pulse, which on traversing the loop causes an injection of chemical transmitter back into the input end of the initial neuron. If these emissions of chemical transmitter are of sufficient quantity, then the pulse can continue to circulate around the loop formed by these neurons.

If the intensity of the signal in the initial neural system is not sufficiently high to initiate the pulses in the return segment of the loop, then the signal quickly disappears. However, as pointed out earlier in this chapter, attention can amplify the intensity of the signal in neurons, possibly by causing an increase in the amount of chemical transmitter ejected per pulse. And attention may thereby cause the signal to continue to circulate in the neural loop for a sufficient time to allow the establishment of the second and third phase memory processes that provide long-time retention of the information.

Long-Term Memory Systems

Much has been learned about the cerebral systems involved in long-term memory by studying people and animals, who, through brain injury or disease, suffer amnesia. A review of the research in this area is presented by Larry R. Squire in his article "Mechanisms of Memory." [16] He points out what has been known for a long time—that bilateral damage to certain areas of the temporal lobe or to the thalamus makes difficult the establishment of new memories or the retrieval of memories stored before the damage event. These areas are not the actual memory banks but operate in conjunction with the cortices where memories are actually stored. There is mounting evidence that damage to the hippocampus and some additional cerebral systems may also interfere with the memory processes. Damage to the various cerebral systems cited does not interfere with the short-term memory processes.

Squire indicates that the view currently emerging, although it is still considered to be hypothetical, is that a given item of memory is stored in the highest level of the specific cortex that processes that item. For example, a visual event is stored in the highest level of processing in the visual cortex. This theory, involving distributed memory sites, calls for a more difficult retrieval task than would a central memory site theory. The retrieval system would have to interact with several memory sites nearly in concert in order to recall a complex event comprised of several modalities of perception and associated thoughts.

One additional system must be noted as part of the memory recall process. When a memory item is being retrieved, sequences of ionic impulses are generated in the neurons involved in the recall process and there are produced associated electric fields. These electrical phenomena must now be transduced into a mental experience of the recalled item by the nonmaterial essence that mediates conscious phenomena.

The Severed Corpus Callosum
and Theories of Self

The severing of the corpus callosum has been found to be effective in curing some people afflicted with epileptic seizures. There are now a number of people who have experienced this operation and who serve as subjects for the investigation of its effect on their behavior. The results of these studies have profound implications for concepts of self.

The severing of the corpus callosum eliminates communication between the right and left hemispheres of the brain and leaves each to attend to its specialization (see chap. 8) unaware of activity in the other hemisphere.

In studying patients who have had this operation, Roger Sperry and others have found that the patients appear to be inhabited by two selves out of direct mental communication with each other.

Sperry describes a typical experiment in which the words "key case" are flashed momentarily in the view of a patient with the word "key" located in the left side of his visual field and the word "case" in the right side of this field.* As a result the word "key" registers in the right hemisphere (the mute side) and the word "case" registers in the left hemisphere (the talkative side). The left hand controlled by the right hemisphere might pick a key out of a pile of objects in front of the patient. The patient, under the influence of the left hemisphere, may say the word "case" or write it with his right hand. He expresses no awareness of what his right hemisphere has perceived or of what it has ordered his left hand to do. When his attention is directed to the behavior of his left hand, a typical response is that he must have done it unconsciously and that his left hand feels numb. Sperry concludes "that in the minor hemisphere we deal with a second conscious entity." [17]

---

* By flashing the words momentarily, acquisition of both words by each hemisphere through eye movement is circumvented. See n. 17.

The belief that a separate consciousness exists in the right hemisphere of patients whose corpus callosum had been severed was supported by further research as described by Sperry in his article (see n. 18) which was published fourteen years after his article published in 1968 (see n. 17). (The subsequent quotations in this section are taken from his 1982 article.) *

In spite of the fact that the Broca and Wernicke areas (which were deemed essential in the understanding, writing, and speaking of language) reside in the left hemisphere of right-handed people, nevertheless, the separated right hemisphere exhibited the ability to comprehend questions selectively directed to it and would respond through nonvocal means such as gestures and acts and the arrangement of blocks displaying letters to form words having as many as four letters. Follow-up interrogation directed selectively at the left hemisphere revealed that it was "incognizant of the answers and performance being ascribed to the right hemisphere." This finding was cited as evidence that the mute right hemisphere has independent language capability.

These further investigations also revealed that the world of the right hemisphere of these patients was "surprisingly well developed"; the right hemisphere possessed a "well-developed sense of self and personal relations along with a surprising knowledgeability in general." It was aware of the person's schedules, the calendar, and the seasons. It recognized and reacted sensibly to personal pictures and pictures of family members.

Although "the more structured and specific informational components of cognitive processing . . . remained confined within the hemisphere within which it was generated, the emotional overtones leaked across to influence neural processing in the other hemisphere." This leakage of emotional

---

* The article referred to in n. 18 is a transcript of a lecture presented by Sperry in Stockholm in 1981 when he received the Nobel Prize in Medicine. He shared this prize with David Hubel and Torsten N. Wiesel.

overtones occurred "apparently through crossed fiber systems in the undivided brainstem" and helped the left hemisphere guess the stimulus to the right hemisphere that evoked the emotion.

Further evidence of cooperation between the two hemispheres may be inferred from the fact that the patient behaved in a well-coordinated manner. If the two hemispheres were completely out of communication with each other, then one might expect the performance of a patient to be replete with conflict. For example, the right leg might try to go north while the left leg goes south, each in pursuit of the separate interests of the left and right hemispheres respectively. Sperry points out, however, that the severing of the corpus callosum of a patient was not "seriously incapacitating as far as ordinary daily activities were concerned." This fact may provide some support for Penfield's conjecture that the center of conscious control resides in the undivided brain stem.

Part Four

Brain-Mind Relationships

Chapter Eleven

The Brain and
the Electronic Computer

The Analogy in Process Between the Brain
and the Electronic Computer

The fact that a neuron fires when a specific activation potential is attained at its input end suggests that it is analogous to the diode in a digital computer. However, there is an important difference. Each diode in current conventional electronic computers receives its activating impulse from a single connecting diode. Conversely, each neuron in the 100 billion complex of neurons in the brain may receive inputs from as many as 1,000 other neurons, some of which make positive contributions and others negative contributions toward the establishment of the activation potential in the subject neuron. Thus the firing of a neuron may respond to a very complex cerebral process.

Although the processes in the electronic computer are very much simpler than those in the brain, nevertheless currently available electronic computers can perform feats that once were thought to be solely capabilities of the human mind. Electronic computers can solve difficult mathematical problems, make decisions regarding complex situations that involve much input data, and can defeat most human opponents in a game of checkers or chess. A detailed discussion of the analogy between the human brain and the electronic computer is given by Dean Wooldridge.[1] So taken is he with the close analogy between the two that he ventures the opinion that it is conceivable that the digital computer may experience a rudimentary form of consciousness.

Learning

Learning through the impact of environment has once been thought to be an exclusive characteristic of living organisms. Learning can now be demonstrated by mechanical devices employing the electronic computer as a brain. A mechanical mouse, for example, has been built that demonstrates this learning ability. The mouse is equipped with wheels and a drive motor, a steering mechanism also coupled with a drive motor, a sensor for detecting the presence of a wall, and a computer with input connections from the sensor and output connections to the drive motors and steering mechanism.

When the mouse is placed in a maze, and its equipment activated, it proceeds down a corridor of the maze until it encounters a wall that blocks further progress. Its sensors send this information to the computer which stores it in its memory, and which also directs the mouse to return and turn into another corridor detected by its sensor. Eventually, the computer learns by trial and error the correct way through the maze, and this information is now stored in its memory. The computer can now direct the mouse successfully through the maze without a single miscue.

The structure of the mouse, complete with sensor, motive equipment, and computer, is the counterpart of the structure of a human as determined by genetic endowment. The mouse's encounters with the wall are the counterpart of the impact of one's environment on oneself. The mouse's behavior may be said to be completely determined by its structural endowment and its environment.

When behaviorists say that the behavior of a person is completely determined by heredity and environment, they are saying, in effect, that the person is a machine differing from the mechanical mouse only in that the person's processes are much more complex. Information from one's sensory systems proceeds through nerves to specific areas in the brain. There the brain processes this information, together with other information in its memory, previously obtained from earlier sensory encounters with one's environment. This processing is prescribed by the manner in which the neurons are interconnected.

On Objective Evidence Regarding Whether Man Is a Machine

Current theories of physical science provide no basis for believing man is anything more than a machine. Nor do they even suggest the possibility that man may be conscious. It is, however, within the realm of possibility that future physical experiments may reveal that some of man's behavior is not mechanistically induced. And, if such evidence is found, then a drastic modification of the physicist's theories of nature would follow.

The most direct experimental approach to determine whether strict mechanistic causality holds in a given system is to install measuring devices at every significant point in the system and determine whether the laws of physics and chemistry, as they are currently conceived, always appear to apply. An experimental investigation of this sort would be easy to apply to the mechanical mouse.

If probes, connected to recording electrical instruments, were inserted into the electrical circuitry of the sensors, motor, and computer of the electrical mouse, the records would show complete causality during its performance. Every electrical pulse at any point in the system would be accountable as the expected result of a pulse somewhere else in the system in accordance with its design and programming. Should a single spurious pulse be observed, it would indicate a malfunction in the system which the designer would try to find and correct.

In a man, similarly equipped with electrical probes in his neural system, neuroscientists do observe correlations between the activity of, say, neurons in the retina of the eye and neurons in the visual cortex of the brain. But the precise accountability of every pulse is lacking. The activity in a cerebral neuron may reflect inputs from as many as 1,000 other neurons. Information transmission and representation appears to involve a statistical process in which contributions of ensembles of neutrons are assessed.

Because it is completely impractical to investigate causality for every neural pulse, it is not feasible either to prove or disprove by this means the thesis that man is a machine differing only in complexity from the mechanical mouse. Unaccountable inputs in some assembly of neurons somewhere in the brain may possibly be the result of a volative thought process. It is improbable that neurological technology will ever attain the sophistication needed to assess statistically the impulses in assemblies of neurons to determine whether all net activities are always causally related or whether there are occasionally, in some areas of the brain, pulse trains that seem to arise spontaneously, and that might be manifestations of the mind imposing its will on the body.

Although mechanists and epiphenomenologists argue that all physiological process data up to the present time support their mechanistic conception of man, the existing data relate to some mechanistically controlled aspect of the human anatomy, and represent only a glimpse into the vast uncharted sea of cerebral processes. Extrapolation from present data to a sweeping generalization concerning all cerebral processes can be highly erroneous. It is not possible on the basis of present cerebral process data to conclude whether or not some control of the body by the mind does occur.

On the Evidence Obtained through Introspection

We must therefore look to other sources of data if we wish to throw some light on the question under consideration.

Much additional insight comes from introspection. It is introspection that leads one to suspect that one is more than merely a more complicated mechanical mouse. Introspection reveals mental experiences like the enjoyment of a multicolored sunset and the fragrance of an orange blossom. Introspection leads to the realization that there exist thoughts and that these thoughts can be the father of one's subsequent acts.

Introspection, in short, reveals the subjective domain, namely, the mind. It is a domain about which the laws of physics and chemistry, the laws of the objective sciences, say nothing. These laws contain no mental parameters. The subjective phenomena are beyond physics; they are nonphysical. Their existence reveals a basic deficiency in the physicist's description of nature. And this deficiency indicates that a device built employing only the knowledge derived from the physical sciences has a negligible probability of being endowed with nonphysical capabilities.

I, therefore, hold that there is a very fundamental difference between the capabilities of the brain/mind and those of an electronic computer. It is more than a difference merely in complexity; it involves a basic phenomenological difference.

The mechanistic aspect of the human contact with the world may be described in terms of streams of neural impulses flowing from sensory systems to the brain. But a person is aware of these inputs to the brain as pictures, sounds, odors, tactile sensations, and other sensory modalities. (These mental experiences with which other people express substantial agreement in their perceptions of the physical world are called "objective data.") This awareness is a personal experience of an "inward" nature, an introspective experience. The awareness of love, hate, pleasure, pain, elation, fear, hope, and desire is also a phenomenon revealed by introspection. And it is through wonder at and excitation by these subjective experiences that science, art, and literature were produced.

It is within the conceivable bounds of physical science, that a machine can be designed and built, which when impacted by molecules emanating from a rose says: "I smell the pleasant fragrance of a rose." But it is obvious that the machine, built out of metal, ceramics, and plastics employing the laws of physical science, has no mental experience of the fragrance of the rose as it mechanically grinds out whatever statement is programmed into it.

Physical science, which is based on "objective" data, describes a nature devoid of mental events. But the phenomena of nature do include mental events, at least to the extent that they occur in the human species. Data on mental events, namely subjective data, can only be obtained through introspection. Introspection is, therefore, a necessary adjunct to objective observations in order to provide a more complete science of nature, in particular with regard to mind-body interactions.

Chapter Twelve

Free Will

On the Decision Process

If the epiphenomenalistic view, that mind is an impotent by-product of the mechanistic process in the brain, is correct, then free will does not exist. If, however, mind is capable of free will, then it must be endowed with energy not bound to mechanistic law.

The issue of free will has long been debated by philosophers to no avail. Authors who have examined the arguments for and against free will have not been able to establish a logical basis for adjudicating this issue. D. J. O'Connor, for example, concludes:

> We have seen that neither the determinist nor the libertarian arguments suffice to establish their case. The determinist extrapolates imprudently from what seems to be established knowledge of the ways in which nature works. The libertarian finds it difficult to state his case in a way that makes it entirely clear what he is claiming and, at the same time, is consistent with reliable scientific knowledge.[1]

Does a person possess free will? If he makes a sensible decision based on good reasons, then it may be argued that his decision was the product of those reasons and hence was not free. If the person does an impulsive act in the face of reason in a moment of abandon, one might say that the person's glandular activity at that moment induced a sense of euphoria that was the cause of the act.

Philosophical attempts to decide the issue of free will rely largely on semantics. Volumes, written by philosophers on this subject, have been eminently unproductive of an irrefutable conclusion. G. E. Moore in his book entitled *Ethics* bases an argument for free will on the meaning of the words "could have." In discussing the statement "I could have walked a mile in 20 minutes . . ." (an act which he did not perform), he holds that "could have" means "could have if I had chosen."

J. L. Austin takes issue with Moore in a lengthy discussion of the meanings of "could have" and "if."[2] And the semantic discussion is continued by P. H. Nowell Smith[3] and Roderick M. Chisholm.[4] Chisholm criticizes Austin's interpretation of the word "if."

But the matter at issue is not what one could have done if one chose but rather what did one actually do at a given instant in time. The determinist argues that what one does at a given instant is completely determined by the environmental and bodily (including cerebral memory content and wiring) conditions that prevail at that instant.[5] And he is not impressed by the claim that one could have done something different at that same instant if one chose. The instant is passed and the claim can never be proven.

A determinist and a libertarian are seated at a table on which rests an apple and an orange. The libertarian says: "I have decided to touch the apple," and he then proceeds to touch it. The determinist remarks that the libertarian's decision to touch the apple was forced by the impact of all of his bodily and environmental factors and was not an exhibition of free will. The libertarian then answers: "To demonstrate that I could have touched the orange, I have now decided to touch the orange" and he touches the orange. The determinist then answers: "Now the conditions impacting on you are different from before. In particular, you have my statement about being forced to touch the apple as an additional input. Your act of touching the orange now reflects these present conditions."

Neither the determinist nor the libertarian can prove his case. There is no way, after an act has been performed, to prove for certain whether or not it was an act of free will. Instead one must study one's own decision-point dynamics.

Philosopher Gilbert Ryle, in arguing against free will states:

> If a theorist speaks without qualms of "volition" or acts of will . . . he swallows whole the dogma that mind is a secondary field of causes. . . . He is also likely to speak of "experiences" . . . to denote the postulated non-physical episodes that constitute the shadow drama on the ghostly boards of the mental stage.[6]

> If ordinary men never report the occurrence of these acts . . . If we do not know how to settle simple questions about their frequency, duration, or strength, then it is fair to conclude that their existence is not asserted on empirical grounds.[7]

My comments on the reality of the mental experiences are given in chapter 2. Ordinary men do on occasion speak of difficult decisions they had to make. The question of interactions between mental and physical events will be discussed in subsequent chapters.

Jerome A. Shaffer concludes his discussion of the freewill issue with the statement: "But the mental cause theorist still owes us an analysis of what it means for something to be under our control."[8]

The discussion of the meaning of "under our control" is the objective of this chapter.

The considerations involved in such a study will be illustrated by the following hypothetical case. I have been offered a position to do research in my field of interest in an institute located in an underdeveloped country. Should I accept this offer?

In favor of accepting, I list the following:

1. The position offers twice my present salary.

2. I am guaranteed complete freedom in the choice of my project.

3. I am offered a position of considerable responsibility and prestige.

4. The adventure of living in a radically different cultural milieu appeals to me.

Against accepting, I list the following:

1. I would be removing my wife and children from family and friends, which would make them unhappy.

2. They may not enjoy or be able to cope with the more primitive environment.

3. My children may not have the benefit of good schooling.

4. I may lose touch with the expanding technology in my field.

What weight shall I place on these several considerations? For guidance I consult a friend who recently returned from a somewhat similar assignment. I seek the reactions of members of my family. I obtain information from the library concerning the country involved. I understand that heredity-cum-environment has some bearing on my thought processes, but I feel no compulsion from this source. My understanding of the implications of my decision leads me to imagine all sorts of future possibilities. A time comes when I must make up my mind. With all these data and thoughts in mind, I strive to make a decision in the best interest of me and my family. As I stand at this decision point, my mind vacillating between "yes" and "no," I do not feel that I am in the grip of a mechanistic force impelling me to a set conclusion. Instead I feel that I am in control, that the responsibility for a wise decision is mine.

This hypothetical scenario illustrates the decision-point trauma that I have on many occasions experienced, where the agony of decision, understanding, imagination, judgment, and a sense of responsibility are at the heart of the process. I identify these decision-point experiences with free will.

Striking a similar note, William Earle wrote:

> The self is no epiphenomenon. The life of the self is a life permeated by choice, and if I do anything, what I am most clearly conscious of is that I am doing it, that I am the agent. . . . I am not always responsible for my doings, and I know usually when I am not. . . . No term could be less adequate to the description of those inner phenomena than "epiphenomenal." The deepest sentiment of self is that nothing can push it around; but if it is an epiphenomenon everything in it is the effect of a push somewhere, a movement of matter, an influence from outside itself.[9]

The Operational Utility of a Belief in Free Will

A consequence of a belief in the reality of free will is the conviction that, to the extent that one's will is the controlling factor, one can predict and order certain future events. I can, for example, predict that the ball that now rests on the floor beneath the kitchen table will an hour from now appear on the top of the table. Precisely at the designated time I grasp the ball and place it on the table.

The concept that the human will is impotent, if sincerely accepted as a guiding principle, induces a passive attitude toward the adventure of living.

Belief in the power of human will, however, motivates people to attempt to build character, acquire desired physical and mental capabilities, strive toward difficult goals, and overcome serious illness. This belief is supported by an impressive body of evidence of great accomplishments through the exercise of will.

Concluding Remarks

Born said that in science "There is no logical path from fact to theory" (see chap. 3). It should come as no surprise that there is no logical path (i.e., the employment of deductive logic) toward adjudication of the issue of determinism vis-à-vis free will. It is a task calling for inductive logic, a task involving a judgmental process applied to the pertinent data.

Admittedly, much human behavior could be classified as deterministic. But to exclude the possibility of the existence of free will, the determinist must show evidence to support his thesis that the mechanistic linkage between cause and effect applies everywhere and always. This he cannot do. The libertarian, however, has the easier task of showing evidence that free will is operative sometimes.

Clever advocates of opposite sides of the free will issue, in reviewing another person's performance that appeared to involve a decision process, can provide substantial rationale in favor of their views, and the discussion ends in a stalemate. The issue cannot be adjudicated by a third-person analysis. It can only be decided by each person for himself by examining his state of mind when he is at the point of making a decision. If one notices at that point that one does not experience a mechanistic compulsion toward a discrete decision, but that reflecting on the assembled information one may experience the agony of indecision in the face of which one is free to make a choice, then it is reasonable to conclude that one possesses free will.

I have examined the free will issue on the basis of those of my subjective experiences of the decision point dynamics in which understanding rather than mechanistic compulsion appeared to be in control. Other people have reported the experience of instances of a similar decision point dynamics. I therefore hold that a theory of the relation between consciousness and matter-energy must account for the phenomenon of free will.

Chapter Thirteen

The Seat of Consciousness

Because of the important roles of the thalamus and the reticular formation as communication and control centers (both of which neural systems reside in the brain stem, see chap. 8), Penfield as well as Thatcher and John suggest that consciousness is associated largely with the processes in the brain stem. Other neuroscientists like Sir Charles Symonds take issue with this view. The subject of the location of consciousness will be explored in this chapter.

On a Diffuse Cerebral Location of Consciousness

Symonds, in a commentary on Penfield's theories on consciousness, which appears as an addendum in Penfield's book, holds that there is no precise location for consciousness in the brain.

> It is a function presumably of synaptic activity, now here and now there. It seems to me more probable that its representation is in the cortex than in the diencephalon having regard to the number of neurons available.[1]

He appears, however, to be somewhat ambivalent on this point because he adds:

> The reticular formation in the brain stem in some way facilitates or "drives" the higher centers, and that in sleep the activity of the reticular formation is inhibited. Here the relationship of consciousness to the brain stem seems well established.[2]

Wooldridge states:

A pinch on the foot, a sound in the ear or a light in the eye produces electric currents in the cortex of the brain that are as
strong and clear when the patient is anaesthetized as when he is
conscious and alert. The patient is unaware of these sensations
only because under the influence of the drug, the reticular system
is unable to send to the cortex and other higher centers of the
brain the specified pattern of electric signals needed to "turn on"
the sense of consciousness.[3]

An interpretation one might draw from this statement is
that the reticular system serves as a neuronal switch that
"turns on" the sense of consciousness at the various cortices
and other higher centers of the brain. This view appears to
be in line with that suggested by Symonds. In this view consciousness shifts its position from one major cortical site to
another with the shift in the focus of neural excitation.

The advantage of this concept is that it suggests an econ-
omy of neural traffic. Visual signals, for example, undergo
very elaborate processing in the visual cortex in the generation of the neural representation of a visual image. The visual
cortex must contain a tremendous amount of information to
represent the very fine detail in form, color, and perspective
that characterizes one's visual images. All this information
would have to be transmitted to the brain stem if consciousness of visual images were located in that area. And this
transfer would require a much more extensive neural link
between the brain stem and visual cortex than would be required if consciousness of the visual image were to occur in
the visual cortex.

Symonds's concept, however, suggests a fragmentation of
consciousness, one consciousness primarily smell-oriented in
the olfactory cortex, another primarily sight-oriented in the
visual cortex, and so forth. Introspection reveals, instead,
that consciousness is a more integrated phenomenon in which
a conscious self can experience various sensory inputs, emo-

tions, and thoughts in concert. This characteristic seems more in consonance with the concept of a central location for consciousness into which the various cortices feed their information, that is, a concept similar to that proposed by Thatcher and John or Penfield. And it is conceivable that the neural connections are sufficient for this task.

On the Central Location of Consciousness

Penfield points out that the neural systems that provide information relating to touch, position, vision, hearing, taste, and smell, each come to the higher brain stem where they synapse with neural systems, which (except possibly for smell) connect with various regions of the neocortex from which neural systems transmit back to the higher brain stem. Neural systems run from the higher brain stem to the motor cortex and then down to the motor cells in the lower brain stem to provide signals for voluntary movements. Pain signals from various points in the body are transmitted through neural systems to the higher brain stem. Neural systems provide transmission of signals from the higher brain stem to the cortices in the neocortex involved with speech and memory. The cortex involved with interpretations also transmits to the higher brain stem. Thus the higher brain stem appears to be a center through which passes all the information that impinges on consciousness.[4] The thalamus, which lies in the diencephalon located in the higher brain stem, is a primary focus for these neural connections.

The reticular formation consists of an assembly of giant neurons that run up the brain stem into the diencephalon. All the neural systems that provide sensory information to the thalamus give off collateral branches that connect with the reticular formation. The reticular formation appears to be involved in the direction of attention. In directing attention the reticular formation may employ the selective signal-enhancing process described in chapter 10. Systems distributed within the thalamus and the reticular formation are involved in the mediation of sleep and arousal.

Thatcher and John associate consciousness with the neural processes in the thalamus and reticular formation with possibly some limited extension in the neocortex. Penfield proposes, more specifically, that the thalamus is the seat of consciousness. He casts the reticular formation in a role subservient to and supportive of the activities in the thalamus.

Penfield points out that his reason for the choice of the higher brain stem over the neocortex as the seat of consciousness stems from his observation that removal of large portions of the neocortex does not destroy consciousness but that "injury or interference with function in the higher brain stem even in small areas would abolish consciousness completely." [6]

The strange performance of people in the throes of a form of epileptic seizure called *petit mal* is cited by Penfield as further support for the thesis that consciousness is seated in the upper brain stem. [7]

In petit mal the attack starts in the temporal or prefrontal cortex with intense neural activity that radiates to the upper brain stem. The resultant selective bombardment of the upper brain stem by neural impulses induces a condition of mindless automism. "In an attack of automism the patient becomes suddenly unconscious, but, since other mechanisms in the brain continue to function, he changes into an automaton." [8] As an automaton he continues to do what he was doing before the seizure or he executes an act already programmed, relying on conditioned reflexes. Penfield cites, among others, the example of a patient who suffered an attack of petit mal while playing a composition on the piano. The patient continued to play the composition in spite of the fact that he was unconscious during the period of the seizure. Subsequently, after recovery, he had no recollection of what transpired during the period of the seizure.

While an automaton, the patient appeared to perform much like the mechanical mouse running the maze. His sensory and nervous systems continued to send signals to his visual, auditory, and somatic cortices, and these signals, following neural pathways previously programmed, caused the proper motor nerve responses, with the patient presumably unaware of any associated visual images, sounds, and tactile sensations. In the state of automism, the patient is unable to make new decisions, to form memories, or to appreciate humor.

The fact that the prefrontal and temporal lobes can be extensively excised without turning the patient into an automaton supports the theory that in the petit mal attack the loss of consciousness is related to the impact of the neural activity on the upper brain stem rather than to the neural activity in the prefrontal or temporal lobes that triggered the seizure.

The science of neurology has not yet advanced to the point where the seat of consciousness may be located with certainty. The hypothesis that consciousness is seated largely in the brain stem suggests an interesting thought. Whatever might have been the combination of structure and processes that represented the spark of consciousness in the brain stem of man's reptilian progenitor, it continued substantially in that location through the various stages in the evolution of *Homo sapiens*. This spark of consciousness grew in its capabilities as evolution provided more elaborate cerebral systems to supply information to the brain stem and to permit greater manipulation of this information.

Consciousness as a Whole-Brain Property

A single cell animal has properties that are different from and greater than the sum of the properties of the molecules of which it is composed. Reasoning along these lines, Sperry proposes that consciousness is a property of the brain operating as a whole, that this property is fundamentally different from the properties of the physical processes of the brain components:

> Basic revisions in concepts of causality are involved, in which the whole, besides being "different and greater than the sum of its parts," also causally determines the fate of the parts, without interfering with the physical or chemical laws of subentities at their own level.[9]

In this view, the brain acting as a whole is cognizant of the implications of the neural activities in its cortices in subjective terms, experienced in concert as phenomena in an integrated consciousness.

Sperry's concept of consciousness as a property of the brain functioning as a whole differs radically from the view held by Symonds that consciousness flits from one cerebral cortex to another as these cortices become energized, and it differs from the views held by Penfield and by Thatcher and John that consciousness is substantially localized in the upper brain stem. Sperry, however, needs to explain how consciousness as an operation of the brain as a whole manages to be sensitive only to the activity in the final cortical staging areas of the various sensations, emotions, and thoughts, and ignores the overwhelming amount of cerebral activity intermediate to the generation of the activity in the final staging areas.

Consciousness as a Nonmaterial Exciter

Science, in effect, posits that there exist NOMEs that embody the fields and laws of physical science and impose their influences on physical objects (see chap. 1). I hold that consciousness is also a NOME that communicates with special areas in the brain to provide for a two-way interaction between brain and mind. On the basis of the information provided by Penfield, I suggest that this NOME may be represented by a field that has its roots in the upper brain stem and is energized by processes in that area. I also suggest that this field extends to those cerebral areas with which it needs to communicate in order to implement the mind-brain interactions.

Chapter Fourteen

Brain-Mind Concepts
Advanced by Neuroscientists

Three of the concepts advanced by neuroscientists, which are described in this chapter, bring to issue the proposition: Is consciousness an impotent by-product of the neural processes of the brain or is consciousness an autonomous entity capable of directing some brain processes to implement its will? One of these concepts, advocated by Thatcher and John, exemplifies the impotent by-product theory. The remaining two, one advocated by Penfield and the other by Eccles, cast consciousness as an autonomous essence. Penfield suggests that consciousness is a manifestation of a special energy that arises in the body through naturalistic processes, while Eccles holds the classical dualistic view that consciousness is a property of a supernatural substance, the soul, instilled into each person by God.

The Hyperneuron

Thatcher and John suggest that the electric field generated by neural activity, largely in the region of the brain stem, constitutes the physical process with which consciousness is associated. They call this electric field the "hyperneuron":

> If we focus our attention not on the membranes of single neurons, but upon charge density distributions in the tissue matrix of neurons, glial cells, and mucopolysaccharide processes, we can envisage a complex, three-dimensional volume of isopotential contours, topographically comprised of portions of cellu-

lar membranes and extracellular binding sites and constantly changing over time. Let us call this volume of isopotential contours or convoluted surfaces a hyperneuron.[1]

To every representational system corresponds a particular distribution of energy, a unique hyperneuron.[2]

And they add that the invariant component of the hyperneuron represents the I in subjective experience, whereas the varying component represents the changing content of the mind.

Thatcher and John visualize the hyperneuron as "isopotential contours." These contours relate to the electric field associated with the charged particles in the brain. As will be described in greater detail in later chapters, the electric field integrates the contributions of all these charged particles and mediates the particle interactions. Therefore the electric field makes a reasonable choice for the essence that embodies consciousness in a mechanistic concept of mind. The term *hyperneuron* is not an apt designation for an electric field because it suggests a neural structure. Consequently I will not use it to designate the mechanistic concept.

As an implication of this theory, Thatcher and John venture to suggest the possibility of artificially creating conscious experiences employing electrical circuitry to generate electric fields similar to those produced in the brain.[3] Wooldridge makes a similar suggestion.[4]

The concept that consciousness is an impotent complementary aspect of the physical activity in the brain appears to be the dominant view in the scientific community. Symonds agrees with a view quoted from the writings of Hughlings Jackson. "Activities of the highest centers and mental states are one and the same thing, or are different sides of the same thing."[5]

In the main, Wooldridge agrees with this epiphenomenolistic view of consciousness and holds that: "No useful purpose has yet been established for the sense of awareness."[6] However, he does have some reservations on this point: "There is nothing in this treatment that is logically inconsistent with the ultimate determination that some small degree of conscious control exists."[7] But one instance of conscious control would destroy the stand of the epiphenomenologists.

On the Potential Field

The potential at any point in the electric field represents the energy required to bring a unit charge from infinity to that point. A surface imagined passing through the points in the electric field having the same potential is called an isopotential surface or, more commonly, an equipotential surface. The total three-dimensional electric field associated with the charge distribution in the brain can be visualized as an assembly of isopotential surfaces. It is this assembly that Thatcher and John call the hyperneuron.

The advantage of associating consciousness with the electric field is that the potential at any given point in the field reflects the field contributions of all the ions and electrons in the brain, giving greatest weight in this summation to the charged particles closest to that point. Thus the field reflects the integrated effects of the electrical activity in and around many neurons. This integration is necessary to endow this activity with some significance because, as discussed in chapter 10, information is conveyed by assemblies of neurons.

It should be noted that the moving electric charges in the brain also generate magnetic fields, and magnetic fields can influence the movements of ions and electrons. But inclusion of the magnetic field in these discussions would not alter the philosophic considerations.

Consciousness as a Manifestation of a Special Energy

After a professional lifetime devoted to research on the brain, Penfield became convinced that his observations could only be explained by the theory that people possess minds that can exercise control over their mental and corporeal processes. This conviction led Penfield to propose that there exists a special energy, the energy of consciousness, and that this energy is seated in and operates through the "highest-brain-mechanism."[8] This special energy is derived by transformation of the electrical energy in the highest-brain-mechanism, but it possesses free will and is not bound to follow the mechanistic laws of electricity.

Penfield locates the highest-brain-mechanism in the upper part of the brain stem within the gray matter of the diencephalon. Mind utilizes the highest-brain-mechanism as its first line of command in marshaling the other cerebral systems to execute the will of the mind. Penfield further proposes that located adjacent to and below the highest-brain-mechanism are two other neural systems that work closely with the highest-brain-mechanism in carrying out its commands. He calls one the "automatic-sensory-mechanism" and the other the "record-of-experience-mechanism."

The highest-brain-mechanism employs the automatic-sensory-mechanism to "coordinate sensory-motor activity previously programmed by the mind. This biological computer mechanism carries on automatically when the highest-brain-mechanism is selectively inactivated."

The highest-brain-mechanism employs the record-of-experience-mechanism to recall stream of consciousness items from the memory storage in the neocortex.

Thus the highest-brain-mechanism with the assistance of the automatic-sensory-mechanism and the record-of-experience-mechanism constitutes the central control system through which consciousness interacts with the neocortex and other cerebral components.

Penfield sees consciousness or mind as a semi-independent energy in the sense that although it depends for its being on the proper functioning of the highest-brain-mechanism, nevertheless, once it is in being, it takes over control and uses the highest-brain-mechanism for its purposes. According to Penfield:

> mind . . . seems to focus attention. The mind reasons and makes new decisions. It understands. It acts as though endowed with an energy of its own. It can make decisions and put them into effect by calling upon various brain mechanisms. It does this by activating neuron-mechanisms.[9]

Because this energy of mind arises by transformation of electrical energy in the brain, it is part of the matter-energy system of nature. I call this energy *vis mentis*. Although Penfield identifies himself as a religious dualist, his concept of mind permits a naturalistic interpretation. The concept of mind as a naturalistic process will be followed in this book.

Sperry also advocates a naturalistic view of the brain-mind relation which "recognizes conscious mental forces as the crowning achievement of evolution" and "gives ideas and ideals control over physico-chemical processes." He suggests "expanding the scope of science to encompass inner experience."[10]

The Classical Dualistic Concept of Mind

In contrast to the concept of mind as part of the matter-energy system of nature classical dualism holds that the mind, as soul, is a supernatural entity which is instilled into the body at birth by God. This point of view is supported by Eccles, who says:

> If we follow Jennings, as I do, in his arguments, and inferences, we come to the religious concept of the soul and its special creation by God.[11]

> I think that, for my personal life as a conscious self, the brain is necessary but not sufficient.[12]

Eccles expounds in some detail on his concept of mind in the book *The Self and Its Brain* which he coauthored with the philosopher Karl R. Popper. In Eccles's view the soul has an organizing, integrating capability that is independent of the processes of the brain. The soul moves through the brain sampling the neural activity in those neural assemblies open to it, much as a bee samples the nectar in a field of flowers. Eccles explains:

> It is proposed that the unity of the conscious experience comes not from an ultimate synthesis in the neural machinery but in the integrating activity of the self-conscious mind on what it reads out from the immense diversity of neural activities in the liaison brain.[13]

> The self-conscious mind selects from these centers according to attention, and from moment to moment integrates its selection to give unity even to the most transient experience.[14]

> Briefly, the hypothesis is that the self-conscious mind is an independent entity . . . that is actively engaged in reading out from the multitude of active centers in the modules of the liaison areas of the dominant cerebral hemisphere.[15]

> . . . it "probes" into the module, reading out and influencing the dynamic patterns of the individual neuronal performances. We can assume this is done from moment to moment over the whole scattered assemblage of those modules processing information of immediate interest (attention) to the self-conscious mind for its integral performance.[16]

By a "module" Eccles means an ensemble of neurons involved in the processing of an item of information. And he points out (as has been discussed in chap. 10) that single neurons "are far too unreliable . . . we emphasize ensembles of neurons . . . acting in some collusive patterned array."[17]

Eccles posits that there exist in the brain "open" modules that can be read out and influenced by the self-conscious mind and "closed" modules that cannot be directly accessed by the self-conscious mind. The information being processed by a closed module is transmitted to the open modules through neural interconnections and is thus made available to the self-conscious mind. The dominant hemisphere contains both open and closed modules. The minor hemisphere contains only closed modules; it transmits its information to the dominant hemisphere through the corpus callosum.

Popper sees reality as consisting of three worlds. World 1 is the physical world (including objects both inanimate and animate and their physical phenomena). World 2 is the world of states of consciousness (sensations, emotions, thoughts, etc.). World 3 is the world of the products of the human mind (e.g., art, literature, science, philosophy, religion). This trialist conception of reality appears at first glance to be an extension of dualism and is accepted as such by Eccles who professes to be a trialist.

An important difference in viewpoint, however, surfaces in the dialogue between Eccles and Popper (contained in Part III of their book) as indicated by the following quotations.

> Eccles: So I am constrained to believe that there is what we might call a supernatural origin of my unique self-conscious mind or my unique selfhood or soul.[18]

> Popper: From an evolutionary point of view, I regard the self-conscious mind an emergent product of the brain.[19]

Popper's view is more in consonance with the naturalistic theories of mind being pursued in this book (in which nature is assumed to include subjective as well as objective aspects) than with classical dualism involving the supernatural. Popper's three worlds might be taken as his classification of the various aspects of nature.

The Holographic Concept

The many enigmas posed by modern scientific theory, in particular those of quantum mechanics and relativity, evoke the thought, as projected by James Haywood Jeans, that there may be an entirely new way of viewing nature that may be more productive of understanding.

In this connection Pribram, a neuroscientist, and Bohm, a physicist, have suggested the holographic concept of the cosmos that is presently receiving considerable attention. This concept will now be examined to determine whether it offers important insights into the relation between consciousness and the physical world.

Pribram's research on the brain, at Stanford University, led him to conclude that the brain stores information in a holographic manner. The precise manner in which this may occur in the brain is not known. This thought was evoked by similarities Pribram observed between certain brain characteristics and the characteristics of photographic holograms.

In the photographic hologram the image of an object or a scene is recorded on a photographic film as a pattern of interference bands made by focusing two streams of laser light on the film; one stream comes directly from the light source, and the other is obtained by reflecting part of the light from the same source to illuminate the object or the scene being photographed. It is a property of a holographic representation that even when a considerable portion of the film is destroyed the entire image of the photographed object or scene may still be obtained by shining laser light through the remainder of the film. In other words the representation of the entire image exists all over the film so that any significant portion of the film contains all the information needed to reproduce the image of the object or scene photographed.

The concept that information in the brain is stored holographically was suggested to Pribram by his finding that when, in excising a tumor, he removes a portion of the patient's brain where memories are stored, the patient does not lose memory content. In contrast, if memory were stored in the brain as it is stored in a filing cabinet, then removal of a portion of the brain would have eliminated the information stored in that portion. In Pribram's concept, each item of memory is stored in three dimensions over the entire volume of the brain's memory bank in a form analogous to the interference patterns of the conventional hologram.

Extension of the Holographic Concept to a Cosmic View

Pribram learned that Bohm was developing a concept of the cosmos as a hologram and the two scientists joined forces in the development of this view. Bohm suggested that the entire cosmos is a hologram encoded in what he calls the *implicate order,* which is considered to be the true reality; it is timeless and spaceless.

The objective world, as man experiences it, represents, according to Bohm, an unfolding of the implicate order into the *explicate order.* This unfolding is analogous to the translation that occurs when utilizing a holographic film through which a laser beam is projected, one sees in space a virtual image of the scene encoded on the film. This observed scene, of course, is an illusion and so presumably also is the explicate order as unfolded from the implicate order in Bohm's cosmology. Bohm's description of many aspects of his cosmology are extremely vague. The reader is referred to his book *Wholeness and the Implicate Order* for a deeper insight than I can convey.[20]

Time, according to Bohm, is a manifestation to man of a sequence of events unfolded from the implicate order which is timeless.

> Both in common experience and in physics, time has generally been considered to be a primary, independent and universally applicable order. . . . Now, we have been led to propose that it is secondary and that, like space. . . , it is to be derived from a higher-dimensional ground, as a particular order. . . . Time re-

lated orders . . . are dependent on a multidimensional reality that cannot be comprehended fully in terms of any time order or, set of such orders.[21]

With regard to the functioning of the hologram, Bohm posits a "holomovement."

> To generalize so as to emphasize undivided wholeness, we shall say that what carries an implicate order is the holomovement, which is an unbroken and undivided totality. . . . It is not required to conform to any particular order, or to be bounded by any particular measure. Thus, the holomovement is undefinable and immeasurable.[22]

The holomovement becomes involved in the unfolding of the explicate order from the implicate order. For example in the discussion of the appearance of the electron in the explicate order, Bohm says:

> Thus, the word "electron" should be regarded as no more than a name by which we call attention to a certain aspect of the holomovement, an aspect that can be discussed only by taking into account the entire experimental situation and that cannot be specified in terms of localized objects moving autonomously through space.[23]

With regard to man's place in the implicate order, Bohm states:

> So it will be ultimately misleading and indeed wrong to suppose, for example, that each human being is an independent actuality who interacts with other human beings and with nature. Rather all these are projections of a single totality.[24]

Bohm sees a union of mind and body in the implicate order as a higher dimensional actuality from which both derive.

> In the implicate order we have to say that mind enfolds matter in general and therefore the body in particular. Similarly, the

body enfolds not only the mind but also in some sense the entire material universe.[25]

Although these several quotations taken out of context give an imperfect representation of Bohm's concept, they nevertheless indicate in a general way the direction of his thinking.

Some Implications of the Oneness of the Cosmos

In the holographic conception of the implicate order, all things are in intimate contact. Or, in Bohm's words, "we come to a new general physical description in which everything implicates everything in an order of undivided wholeness." This view has implications both in the fields of science and parapsychology.

Fundamental particles, that is, electrons and photons, when they encounter a special apparatus, display interference patterns. The interpretation of this phenomenon suggested by physicists of mystical persuasion, like Bohm and Capra, is that each particle passing through the apparatus knows what previous particles have done and acts accordingly. Present conventional models of nature provide no explanation of this phenomenon. The concept of "undivided wholeness" in the holographic model "explains" this phenomenon by asserting that all the particles and the apparatus are in intimate contact in the implicate order where the whole process is mediated. But no explanation is offered regarding how this process in the implicate order is implemented.

Parapsychological phenomena, for example, mental telepathy and psychokinesis, may also be explainable as events in the implicate order, where all minds and all objects are conjoined in undivided wholeness.

Science provides no model that explains even the simplest of phenomena. No explanation is offered on how the sun, separated from the earth by 93 million miles of essentially empty space, can influence the motion of the earth. Science is content to invent a word to designate a force in nature and to provide equations whereby its effect on the behavior of objects can be predicted. If one is content with this limitation of science, then it is not clear why it is necessary to depart from this procedure for the behavior of fundamental particles.

Remarks on Holographic Cosmology

Plato, in his book the *Republic,* portrays the condition of humanity at large as being analogous to that of men chained inside a cave and permitted to see the realities outside the cave as shadows cast on the wall of the cave by light streaming through a window over the heads of the men. This analogy is meant to mark figuratively man's imperfect insight into nature as limited by his sensory endowments.

Inspired men have tried to transcend their sensory limitations by flights of imagination. The holographic concept is one such attempt. In it a person is a union of mind and body in an obscure reality, the implicate order.

The holographic concept, however, provides no basis for investigating mind-body relationships. The "holomovement," which relates to processes in the implicate order, is "undefinable and immeasurable."

It is more productive, in the pursuit of mind-body relationships, to view physical objects and the NOMEs that move them as realities in a this-world conception of nature. Although the mode of existence of the NOMEs, of which mind is a member, and their means of interacting with physical objects are hidden from human perception, nevertheless some insight into their influences can be inferred from observations in both the physical and mental domains. These influences, systematized, represent a useful science that can include mind-body relationships.

I am sympathetic to all imaginative attempts to transcend the limitations of the human sensory systems. Even those concepts that are flawed may contain some element that may inspire other minds to conceive ideas closer to the truth. But each concept must be subjected to the test of reason. In addition to the fact, as previously pointed out, that holographic cosmology lacks operational utility, I find objectional its fatalistic implication. If all substance and minds are inscribed in the implicate order in timeless oneness, then the future is already prescribed, and all of man's aspirations and efforts to achieve are as an empty charade. This concept degrades humans to puppets, and their existential experience to a puppet show in which they act out a scenario timelessly inscribed in the implicate order.

Part Five

Discussion of the Mechanistic Theory of Consciousness (The Impotent Mind Theory)

Chapter Fifteen

Some Physical Considerations Relating to the Mechanistic Theory

Relation Between the Electric Field and the Charged Particle Distribution in the Brain

Before proceeding with a critique of the theory that consciousness is a complementary aspect of the electric field, it is pertinent to examine the relation between the electric field and the charged particle distribution in the brain. Insight into this relationship contributes to an understanding of some of the advantages and limitations of the proposed theory.

The electrical potential at any point in the brain, such as a point in the hyperneuron, can be computed from the distribution of electric charges in the brain. An electron has a charge of $-1a$ (where $a = 4.80 \times 10^{-10}$ esu). A proton has a charge of $+1a$. A neutral molecule, in which there are as many electrons as there are protons, has a net charge of zero. An ion is an atom or molecule that possesses a charge by virtue of the fact that the number of electrons in the particle is either more or less than the number of protons; if an excess of electrons exist, the ion bears a negative charge; if a deficiency of electrons exists, the charge on the ion is positive. The numerical value of the charge on the ion is equal to the difference between the number of electrons and protons. If, for example, a molecule lacks two electrons, it is a positive ion with a charge of $+2a$.

The electrical potential at any given point A in the brain

due to any given charged particle is equal to the value of the charge divided by the distance of the charged particle from point A. The total electrical potential at point A due to all the charged particles in the brain is simply the sum of the potentials due to the individual particles, each computed in the manner described. In this summation, potentials due to negative charges are subtracted from potentials due to positive charges. The equipotential surface is an imaginary surface that is the locus of all points having the same net potential value. The electric field may be visualized as an array of such imaginary equipotential surfaces, each surface representing a different value of electrical potential.

On the Integrating Feature of the Electric Field

Information is transmitted in the brain by imposing the same train of impulses on an ensemble composed of many neurons. These trains of ionic impulses are in synchronism and cooperate to produce a charge representation that is large compared with that produced by pulses that are at random with respect to one another in the various neurons of the ensemble. The electric potential field produced by this charge representation reflects in its magnitudes and contours this discrimination in favor of coherent impulse trains.

The flow of uncharged chemical transmitters can affect the electrical field only by influencing the electrical processes in the neurons.

On the Charged Particle Distribution

Because every charged particle in the brain can provide some increment to the electric field at every point in the brain, there must build in the final staging area of a sensory system (for example, the final staging area of the representation of a picture in the visual system) an ionic representation that is so large that the inputs from other ionic areas would have a negligible effect on the associated electric field. Otherwise, the picture in this example would contain much extraneous activity. Furthermore this ionic representation must change fast enough to reflect the changes in the information.

Even a small item of information, as, for example, the word *the* in the auditory process, is transmitted through the neural systems as a large sequence of ionic impulses with its special spacing between impulses. Although these impulses arrive at the final staging area sequentially, the ionic edifice being built must retain the effects of these impulses including their spacings in order that consciousness, as a complementary aspect of the associated electric field, may experience the item of information as a unit. The ionic edifice must adjust its configuration as new items of information displace old.

The ionic edifices probably build up in the glial cells and the saccharides that surround the neurons in the final staging areas. Penfield holds that these areas lie in the upper brain stem. Other neuroscientists suggest that they may be more diffusely located in the neocortex. In view of the intense electric fields associated with these areas, it may be feasible to locate them employing electrical devices.

If the electric fields representing the various sensory modalities were isolated from one another, these modalities would be experienced as mental states in separate consciousnesses that were unaware of one another's existence. For consciousness to be a unitary phenomenon, in the mechanistic theory under discussion, substantial merging of these electric fields would be required.

Chapter Sixteen

Critique of Mechanistic Theories of Mind

On the Mechanism of Mind

Thatcher and John suggest that the ionic edifices and associated electric fields described in the previous chapter are the means for generating mental experiences. These ionic edifices are each located at the final staging area of a sensory system. The kind of mental experience induced is determined by the movements and convolutions of the field. Certain of these movements and convolutions provide mental experiences of pictures, others of sound, others of odor, and so forth. The locations of these ionic edifices and electric fields may be controversial, but it would be difficult to suggest a different mechanism in the brain for performing the task of generating mental experiences.

One might be tempted to draw an analogy between the brain and a television set. Electric energy enters and is processed by the circuitry of the television set. Some of it proceeds to the video tube where it paints a picture, and some of it proceeds to the speaker where it produces sound. However, in the television set there is a mechanism specifically designed to produce pictures and an entirely different kind of mechanism for producing sound. In the brain, the various mental effects are produced by basically the same kind of mechanism. This is a remarkable feat that warrants further consideration.

146

Complementarity

In this mechanistic theory of mind, mental events are complementary aspects of the electric field and nothing more. For each electric field configuration in the final staging area of a sensory system, there is a complementary mental experience. This mental experience cannot affect the processes of the brain and must change when the field contours change. The mind in this theory has no memory of its own.

These limitations pose a problem for the mechanistic theory of mind. When a person is listening to a lecture and as each item of information impacts on the electric field in the final staging area of the auditory system, there occurs in the mind the stated item. When this item is displaced by the next item, it cannot be recalled by the mind. Thus the mind has no way of synthesizing a sequence of phrases into a sentence or a series of sentences into a concept.

The machinery of the brain may store all of the items in its memory bank and by recalling them reconstruct the entire statement. But the mind does not benefit from this retrieval because as each item of the recalled statement again passes through the final staging area, the mind hears only one item at a time and cannot grasp the complete statement. This recall, according to the mechanistic theory, is not stimulated by the mind, but rather by some mechanistic impulse in the brain. The concept of complementarity appears to take the mind out of the thought process.

Introspective examination of one's process of understanding a lengthy sentence or paragraph that one is reading leaves one with some feeling of skepticism regarding the mechanistic theory. One proceeds, in the reading, from one phrase to the next as each phrase enters one's understanding. And, as one progresses through the statement, earlier phrases begin to recede from one's consciousness. When one has completed the reading, one has a sense that he understands what the writer said even though he does not remember the precise wording of the statement. When asked to explain what the writer said, one does not give a machinelike replication of the writer's precise wording but rather one renders the idea in his own words and employs different combinations of words each time one attempts the explanation.

Often a person's explanation of a writer's thoughts indicates that he has not precisely captured the idea or that the writer's words have stimulated additional ideas. Great poetry evokes mental imagery far beyond the meaning of the words. There appears to be more to the impact of words on one's mind than the mere mechanical complementary response to charged particle representations, as each phrase engages one's attention.

Holistic and Discriminatory Capabilities of the Mind

It was pointed out in the previous chapter that, in order for consciousness to be a unified experience of all impacting sensory modalities, it is necessary that the contours of the hyperneuron reflect the representation of all of these inputs. But the holistic and discriminatory processes needed by the mind to properly interpret the significance of the hyperneuron poses a problem to a theory in which mind is a complementary aspect of the hyperneuron and nothing more.

The electric potential at a given point A in the hyperneuron may have, for example, a value of 20 millivolts (mV). There is no denotation at point A that this value is the resultant of contributions of, for example, 10 mV from the visual cortex, 7 mV from the auditory cortex, and 3 mV from the olfactory cortex. Neither is there any denotation at A that the potential at point B is, for example, 17 mV, at point C is 25 mV, at point D is 12 mV, and so forth. If consciousness is related to the electric field point-by-point then it can only reflect the field point-by-point. Under these circumstances, consciousness has no holistic or discriminatory capabilities.

If, nonetheless, we assume that the conscious experience can make holistic and discriminatory appraisals of the field, we are crediting consciousness with capabilities for which there is no mechanistic underpinning, and we have departed from the concept that consciousness is merely a complementary aspect of the electric field. For example, while the electric potential distribution at the "now" instant is fixed, consciousness must be busy comparing values at various points and making holistic and discriminatory appraisals. If we hold that consciousness can perform these functions, then we have said that consciousness is more than the complementary aspect of the field. We have placed a ghost in the machine.

Consciousness as an Aspect of the Total Brain Process

Let us now consider the proposition that consciousness is associated with the operation of the brain as a whole, and that the brain may transcend in properties those of the component parts of the system. Could the brain system as a whole possess the capability of holistically viewing its operations and discriminating portions of these operations as separate sensory modalities?

The thesis that the whole has properties that transcend the properties of its parts is often illustrated by the fact that the properties of water differ radically from the properties of the hydrogen and oxygen atoms of which the water is composed.

The hydrogen and oxygen atoms possess electric fields of very intricate shapes. These fields are responsible for binding the hydrogen and oxygen atoms together to form molecules of water and for binding water molecules together to form a liquid. If the shapes of the electric fields associated with the hydrogen and oxygen atoms and the changes in these field shapes as the atoms join to form water were known, one could, in theory, determine the properties of water. The properties of electric fields are adequate for accounting for the properties of water that transcend the properties of its components.

When we look for the physical phenomenon in the totality of the brain processes which provides communication between these processes to achieve their holistic representation, we again come to the electric field. Thus whether we consider the electric field in the brain as a whole or the electric field in some special part of the brain, the same fundamental problems apply. As previously pointed out, consciousness as an impotent complementary aspect of the electric field does not have in itself the dynamics for the required holistic and discriminatory appraisals of the field to provide the associated mental experiences. We must look for something other than the electric field to account for the phenomena of consciousness.

Sperry views consciousness as a property of the brain functioning as a whole. But he says: "The events of inner experience . . . become themselves explanatory causal constructs in their own right, interacting at their own level with their own laws and dynamics." He is divorcing conscious processes from the rigid mechanistic laws of electricity that underlie brain processes. He is, in effect, calling for a new energy with its special laws.

The Thought Process

Mechanists contend that man's process of thinking is analogous to that of a computer and that the sequence of supposed logically-related thoughts are merely statements made to reflect the situation at special points, like decision points in the process. The process goes on mechanistically, but because his thoughts are logically related, a person is deluded into thinking that his mind is in control of the process.

This mechanistic analogy will be illustrated by considering the performance of an electronic computer programmed to determine the answer to the question: What number, when added to its square, produces a value of 7? The machine is trying to determine the value of X in the algebraic equation $X + X^2 = 7$.

The computer is programmed to solve this equation by trial. It substitutes a value of 1 in this equation and finds that the corresponding value of $X + X^2$ is 2. It is programmed to compare this value with 7 and finding that it is too low decides to try a value of X of 2. It is a simple matter to construct and program the machine to say when it tries the value of 1: "I will now try a value of 1." When it obtains the result 2 and compares it with the desired value of 7, the machine says: "The value 2 obtained in this trial is less than 7. I will try a value of 2 for X." The machine computes $X + X^2$ for $X = 2$ and obtains a value of 6. The machine says: "This value is less than 7. I will try $X = 3$." The computation with this value of X produces a value for $X + X^2$ of 12. The machine compares this value with the desired value of 7 and says: "I have tried the value of 3 for X and it has produced a result of 12 which is now higher than the desired value of 7. Therefore I will try a value of 2.5 which is halfway between the last two trials for X." In this way the machine can progressively come closer to the correct value for X.

It is noted that at each decision point in the computation the machine has made a pertinent statement about the situation and has made a logical decision on what to do next. If the machine had a mind which was aware of the significance of these statements, this mind might be convinced that it is in control of the process because of the thread of logic that appears to run through the sequence of statements.

Man's brain as a machine is much more complex than an electronic computer and is capable of much more exotic operations. But mechanists say that the difference between the brain and the computer is basically quantitative. They hold that the stream of thoughts in the brain are reflections of the status of the processes in the brain as they run their mechanistic route in accordance with the logic programmed into the brain. If this is true, then no feedback from the meanings in the conscious state to a subsequent effect on the neural processes in the brain is required.

But this passive role of consciousness, in which thoughts pop into one's mind in logical sequence as neuronal processes run their mechanistic course, does not appear to agree with one's actual experiences while engaged in an analytical thought process. Instead, one is aware of actively striving to reach for the new idea, guided by an unexpressed feeling for what it might be. One is aware of purposely directing the search for words and sentence structure, continuously modifying both, until one's mind is satisfied that it has accurately portrayed the idea.

Machines can express ideas only relevant to aspects of processes for which they have been programmed. The example of the machine solving the mathematical problem previously cited indicates how tightly bound to programmed processes the ideas of the machine are. The minds of men, through their creativity, can break through to new ideas for which no mind had been programmed. Newton's laws of mechanics and Einstein's theory of relativity are examples of such creative breakthroughs.

The Significance of Understanding

In addition, the mechanistic view of thought cannot account for one's personal subjective experience of "understanding" and its impact on one's brain processes.

The importance of understanding was brought home to me by an incident in my early youth. When I was thirteen years old, I was introduced, as most high school freshman are, to the subject of algebra. The transition from arithmetic to the more abstract concepts of algebra was difficult for me. In particular I had little understanding of what an equation like $A + B = C$ meant. I learned, by rote, rules for manipulating equations. I applied these rules with indifferent success and barely achieved a passing grade in the course.

The following year, with practically no understanding of algebra, I had even less success with geometry. I failed every monthly examination. One evening while studying for the final examination I suddenly experienced a flash of understanding. Although that incident occurred over sixty years ago, its emotional impact is still vivid in my memory. I remember the appearance of the room and the table at which I was seated. But above all I remember the intensity of my elation at this breakthrough to understanding.

The idea that flashed into my mind, and it was a very simple idea, gave me, for the first time, an understanding of what an equation says. The idea was this: the letters that appear on each side of an equation represent numbers whose values, prior to the solution of the equation, are as yet unknown. If the numerical values of the letters were known, then substitution of these values for the letters and evaluation of each side of the equation leads to the same numerical value on both sides of the equation; in other words the equation would reduce, for example, to a statement like $4 = 4$ or $5 = 5$, and the like. Therefore, in order to maintain this equality, while manipulating an equation, one must treat both sides alike. The rules of manipulation I had learned by rote now made sense.

Simple as this flash of understanding seems, it had a major effect on my subsequent behavior. I immediately went back through my algebra and geometry books and proved the various theorems without the assistance of the explanations in the books. I passed the final geometry examination with a perfect grade much to the astonishment of my teacher.

The intense emotional impact of that moment of understanding drove me, while still in high school, to obtain books on trigonometry, calculus, college algebra, and vector analysis, which I read avidly, enthralled by the power of the logic of mathematics. My fascination with mathematics continued through college and led to my choice of a career.

This subjective experience of understanding and its subsequent effect on my performance is a phenomenon that the electronic computer cannot share as it mechanically grinds out solutions to a mathematical problem precisely as it is programmed. Neither would a consciousness tied point by point to an electric field in the brain have any mechanistic basis for the experience of the moment of understanding and its subsequent impact on the brain processes that mediate behavior.

In man's zeal to attain new vistas in the sciences, music, literature, philosophy, and art, and in his creative activities in general, it is "understanding" that is at the heart of his efforts. It is "understanding" that inspires and guides him. It is "understanding" that tells him when he has attained a significant goal. And it is "understanding" that generates exultation on this attainment.

Volition

The subject of free will versus determinism was previously discussed on philosophical grounds. A position was taken in favor of free will employing inductive logic, and this conclusion is of course subject to the limitation that it can be negated if new adverse evidence is uncovered. The subject will now be reviewed in the context of neurological considerations and the mechanistic theory of consciousness.

A simple manifestation of free will is one's ability to direct one's attention. There are, of course, many instances when one's attention is triggered automatically. It can be done by a sudden unusual sensory input. For example, while reading a book one is only dimly aware of background music coming from the radio; suddenly one hears an explosion or the cry of a baby in the next room. Immediately one's attention is directed toward one's auditory inputs and one listens for further sonic information.

There is possibly a mechanistic explanation for this shift in attention. In the case of the explosion, the sharp increase in the signal to the auditory cortex may shift attention to that sensory modality. Thatcher and John indicate "that a complex functional organization exists which can modulate the effectiveness of afferent input. . . . The system can selectively enhance the signal-to-noise ratio of events in a particular sensory modality."[1] Currently it is not certain how this amplification by attention is accomplished. It was speculated in chapters 7 and 10 that somehow attention causes an increase in calcium ions in the neurons of the sensory system under surveillance, which causes an increase in the chemical transmitter output at their synapses with other neurons that transmit the information to the brain. This whole process from the increase in noise caused by the explosion to the amplification of signals coming from the auditory system may be purely mechanistic.

One can conceive of many instances, however, when the shift of attention does not appear to be mechanistically induced. For example, just to make this philosophical point, I can proceed, at a moment of my choosing, to focus my attention sequentially on what I am seeing, hearing, smelling, the pressure on my right toe, the tension in my left hand, and myriad other sensory inputs, most of which at the time of the demonstration would not have called for special attention. I can see my bookcase as a whole and, at will, can focus my attention on any special book and read its title. I can hear a babel of voices coming from the next room and, at will, can focus my attention on what my wife is saying. And I can then return my attention to my thoughts and let all these sensory inputs go largely unattended.

Was my desire to make this philosophical point, and the subsequent demonstration of the arbitrary shifting of my attention through this inconsequential series of sensory inputs, merely the by-products of the neural activity generated by the "complex functional organization" described by Thatcher and John? My judgment leads me to reject this proposition for the following reasons.

Electrical impulses travel through nerves at a speed of between 1 and 300 feet per second. Thus there is a lag between the time the impulses start through myriad nerves involved, and the time the electric field is established that has as its by-product the thought: "I desire to illustrate a philosophical point by willfully evoking a sequence of attention focusing phenomena." At the start of these neural impulses the desired electric field state did not yet exist and, therefore, according to the mechanistic theory, neither did the thought exist. Then, without the thought providing the motivation, how did the proper neural pulses start that eventually culminated in the generation of this thought?

There was no physiological necessity for this thought, nor for the subsequent arbitrary sequence of inconsequential acts of attention focusing. Thus one cannot point to sensory inputs as the physical phenomena that triggered the neural impulses which culminated in the thought and the attention-focusing acts. It appears unreasonable to believe that my neural system was correctly preprogrammed to generate the very elaborate series of neural pulses that had as their ultimate consequence the construction of the electric fields that represented in proper sequence my philosophical thoughts and attention focusing acts.

After his many experiments on patients, in which he used an electrified probe to stimulate various points in their brains, Penfield reports that he was never able to override a patient's awareness of the exercise of his own will. For example, if, by applying the probe to some point in a patient's brain, he caused the patient to move a part of his body, the patient was never of the impression that it was a volitive act. The patient would say: "You made me do it." Man is intensely aware of his volitive power.

Some philosophers of epiphenomalistic persuasion argue against the autonomous mind theory and for the mechanistic mind theory on the basis of their interpretation of the implications of neurological data. For example, Jerome Shaffer, following a line of reasoning employed by T. H. Huxley, argues:

> So far, developments in neurophysiology have consisted in discovering more and more cases in which brain events are causes. And we have every reason to believe that future developments in the field will be consistent with this trend, so that eventually we can assume, by extrapolation, that all brain events and concomitant mental events will be explainable in terms of brain events. On the other hand we have no experimental evidence to show that mental events, by themselves, ever effect other mental events, and we have no reason to think that future developments will give us such evidence. . . . And that means that it is more reasonable to accept epiphenomenalism than to believe in interactionism.[2]

This argument is seriously flawed. Present neurological data, impressive as it is, represents only a minute fraction of the information needed to understand the processes of the brain. The history of science indicates that the extrapolation from a minute amount of known data to a sweeping generalization runs the risk of grave error. As pointed out in chapter 11, the kind of experiments needed to decide the issue on the basis of neurological data are far beyond current technology and indeed may never be feasible.

In making the statement that "we have no experimental evidence to show that mental events, by themselves, ever affected other mental events" Shaffer disregards evidence provided by introspection. It is only through introspection that Shaffer, and people in general, know of the existence of mental events. And it is through introspection that one is aware of many instances when one thought provokes another. One is never aware of the operation of the machinery of the brain in this connection. Introspection leads one to the belief that the machinery of the brain is functioning as an agent of the mind and not as the originator of a sequence of thoughts. One cannot ignore introspection in discussing mental events.

The mind has other special features revealed by introspection that cannot be explained as the products of the mechanistic grindings of the machinery of the brain. The mind is curious; it wants to know what lies beyond the horizon or what causes lightning or cancer. The mind sees beauty in form and sound and creates art, literature, and music for the enjoyment of other minds. The mind sees humor in statements and situations and creates humorous stories for the entertainment of other minds. The mind seeks a reason for being to satisfy a yearning for a purposeful life.

Part Six

Discussion of the Vis Mentis Theory of Consciousness (The Autonomous Mind Theory)

Chapter Seventeen

Energy of Mind as a Component of Nature

The Basis of Energy of Mind

It is conventional scientific practice to postulate a new energy form when a phenomenon not explainable in terms of other energy forms is observed. The strong force in the nucleus of an atom was postulated, for example, to "explain" why the nucleus is not disrupted by the mutual repulsion between its protons. In the same spirit Penfield posited the existence of energy of mind when it became apparent to him that many of his observations made in the course of his neurological research could not be explained in terms of the electrical processes in the brain.

Energy transformations are usual events in the physicist's world. Electrical potential energy transforms into kinetic energy and vice versa as two electrons recede from or approach each other. Just as electrical potential energy follows laws that differ from those followed by kinetic energy, so also it is reasonable to expect that the energy of mind has its special laws that differ from those for electrical energy.

Thus energy of mind, if it is indeed found to exist, takes its place among other energy forms in a this-world conception of reality rather than as the equivalent of the soul in the classical dualistic conception.

Penfield, in making the statement concerning the energy of mind, "The form of that energy is different from that of the neuronal potentials that travel the axone pathways,"[1] felt

161

that he was guilty of espousing scientific heresy. He said: "I fear to run the risk of hollow laughter from the physicists." [2] But this fear is not shared by physical scientists.

A suggestion similar to that of Penfield's was made by the eminent chemist Wilhelm Ostwald (Nobel prize, 1909).

> The energy of the central nervous system governs consciousness. . . . The energy connected with consciousness is the highest and rarest form of energy known to us. It is only produced in specially developed organs, and even in the brain of different people. . . . We must not be surprised that such energy is only produced under special circumstances. . . . It is generally possible to transform a given quantity of energy into another form without any measurable part of the former remaining. . . . I must stress that this is only a tentative opinion; for a scientific decision of the matter a great deal of work of the most difficult kind is still needed. [3]

It is interesting that, at a time when neuroscientists are loathe to break with what they consider to be orthodox physical theory, the physicists are expressing dissatisfaction with their mechanistic view of nature, and some are embracing Eastern mysticism.

According to Capra, a theoretical physicist and a spokesman for this trend of thought among scientists,

> . . . the two foundations of twentieth-century physics—quantum theory and relativity theory—both force us to see the world very much in the way a Hindu, Buddhist or Taoist sees it. [4]

In contrast to Capra's break with orthodox science, the suggestion that the mind is a manifestation of a new form of energy is, as I have previously indicated, in line with the usual practice in physical science of proposing a new form of energy when phenomena, not explainable by presently accepted energy forms, are encountered.

Vis Mentis and the Conservation of Energy

The argument is often advanced that if one's mind is capable of ordering movement of one's body, then the law of conservation of energy would be violated. However, the argument presupposes that the only legitimate energies to be considered in the conservation law are the energies already specified by the physical sciences. Andrsej Trautman, however, in his essay "Conservation Laws in General Relativity," points out:

> The process of generalizing the law of conservation of energy by introducing new kinds of energy is characteristic of the whole development of physics. The same can be said of other conservation laws.[5]

It is, of course, not certain that energy of mind is subject to the conservation law. The conservation law is empirically based. Hermann Weyl states that even in the physical domain

> no aprioristic command would prevent physics from abandoning the strict validity of the conservation laws if that should become necessary under the pressure of new empirical discoveries.[6]

The Expansion of Physical Science to Encompass Mental Phenomena

The physical scientists completely ignore data on subjective experiences obtained through introspection. Consequently, they are looking at only a small part of the natural scene. They ignore the fact that even the sensory data that lie at the basis of their theories and the processes of thought that produced these theories are revealed to them through introspection.

They reduce things into elementary particles and, by finding the laws relating to these particles, they hope to understand the whole. But the elementary particles of all things are inanimate. It is therefore not surprising that the physical scientists have evolved a purely mechanistic conception of the universe from their reductionistic approach.

To bring mind into this mechanistic conception of the universe, it was necessary to propose that it is merely a complementary aspect of the physical processes in the brain. But this theory, as indicated in chapter 16, does not adequately account for the remarkable capabilities of the human mind. The complementarity concept did not satisfy neuroscientist Eccles and he calls for an expansion of the scientific approach:

> It has been proposed that the problem of brain and mind can be resolved by assimilating it to the Principle of Complementarity. I personally am not satisfied by this ingenious maneuver, though it may point the way to a more radical solution. I seem dimly to apprehend the necessity for some revolutionary concept in psycho-physiology that would be equivalent to the Theory of Relativity in Physics.[7]

In order for the scientist to include mind within his perspective, he must acknowledge from the start that all of his scientific data are given to him as mental experiences of sights, sounds, odors, and so forth, and that the existence of these mental phenomena are completely outside the purview of a science based on the so-called objective observations on the behavior of inanimate objects. He must also accept the existence of his thoughts as natural phenomena, because it is through these thoughts that his theories are evolved.

The physical scientist's reluctance to accept the existence of mind as an entity in nature is based on the impression that only material objects exist. But, as I have pointed out in chapters 1, 5, and 6, the description of nature provided by the physical scientist projects the existence of two realms of being. In one realm, the material realm, lie the physical objects of nature, and in the other realm, the nonmaterial realm, lie the exciters that move these objects. These exciters are represented by scientists in terms of mathematical equations that define a set of energies and additional equations that prescribe the interactions of these energies with the physical objects.

The mode of existence of these NOMES is a mystery; it is hidden from human perception. The existence of these exciters and their interactions with physical objects are all inferred from the movements of these objects.

Mind is a NOME

I propose that consciousness, or mind, with its content of mental events is a NOME, and that its laws of interaction with the physical world be derived from observed correlations between mental and physical events.

I perform the following simple experiment. I stand before a mirror in which I see my face and I command my eyelids slowly to close. I see them close and as they close my vision dims. I conclude that a physical event, the lowering of my eyelids, has caused a mental event, the dimming of my vision. The thought that I desire to illustrate a philosophical principle was followed by the command to lower my eyelids and the subsequent lowering of the eyelids. These observations indicate that a mental event can cause another mental event and also a physical event. I can perform many experiments of the kind described which reenforce the conclusion that mental phenomena can interact with physical phenomena and can cause other mental phenomena.

The set of energies and associated laws specified by physical scientists represent the present method whereby these scientists deal with phenomena in the physical domain. Because the mind also interacts with the physical domain, I propose that the method of physical science be extended to include a mental energy and its laws—vis mentis, energy of mind.[8] It must be emphasized that these energies and laws are not the NOMEs that they represent, but are merely part of a scheme devised to investigate phenomena mediated by these NOMEs. Like the NOMEs of physical science, the mode of existence of the NOME called mind, and the means whereby it interacts with physical objects are mysteries.

Chapter Eighteen

On the Interaction Between Brain and Mind

Res Mentis

In the vis mentis theory it is posited that the energy of mind is generated naturalistically by the transformation of physical energy in the brain into vis mentis. I call the special structure in the brain that mediates this transformation *res mentis*.

Where in the brain is res mentis located? Penfield points out that the excising of large portions of the neocortex does not destroy consciousness, but that even a small intrusion into the upper brain stem does extinguish consciousness. The upper brain stem is involved in arousal from sleep and in the directing of attention. Massive infusion of neural excitation into the upper brain stem (as in a case of petit mal) causes a loss of consciousness. These considerations indicate that res mentis is probably located in the upper brain stem. It also appears that when res mentis ceases to make the required energy transformation because of interference with its operation or depletion of its physical energy then consciousness also ceases.

If res mentis were involved not only in the generation of vis mentis but also in the two-way interactions between vis mentis and the cerebral processes, then it would be expeditious for the final staging areas of the physical representations associated with the various mental events to be in the upper brain stem near res mentis. However, if vis mentis, once established, operates with the cerebral systems independently of res mentis, then it is conceivable that it might reach out to these final staging areas even if they were more diversely located in the cortex.

On the Field of Vis Mentis

In physical science the gravitational potential energy field is portrayed graphically as a set of isopotential contours computed from a mathematical equation. This portrayal is an inadequate representation of the NOME that mediates gravitational phenomena. It lacks a representation of the equation that describes the acceleration of an object within that field, the equation that also takes into account the kinetic energy of the object and describes the resultant motion of the object, and the means whereby the NOME acts on the object to move it. Nonetheless, this graphical portrayal of gravitational energy is found to be useful.

It may also prove to be useful to represent vis mentis graphically as a field with the understanding that both vis mentis and its field are inadequate representations of the NOME that embodies mind and mediates its interactions with the brain. The field is a graphic representation of the physical extent of the zone of influence of the NOME and by its structure may represent a property of the NOME. But mental experiences and initiative lie in the invisible domain of the NOME. Graphically, the field may be visualized as emerging from the upper brain stem and running to those areas of the brain and body involved in interactions with the mind.

It is sometimes convenient to say that vis mentis senses, emotes, and thinks, when I mean that the hidden NOME in nature called consciousness is engaged in these mental acts. Physical science provides precedence for this mode of discourse. It is common practice, for example, to say that a planet is constrained to follow a path around the sun by the sun's gravitational field, when one means that the hidden exciter in nature, which is represented by the physicist's equations for this field and its effect on matter, is responsible for this feat.

Brain and Mind Dynamics

The characteristics to be ascribed to vis mentis must relate to the dynamics of the mind and its interaction with the dynamics of the brain.

Stored in the memory bank of my brain is a large dictionary of words whose presence and meaning can be brought forth at the demand of the mind. When each word is recalled, it is released to the neural pathways of the brain as its special sequence of neural impulses, analogous to the special sequence of electrical impulses whereby a word would be transmitted through a telegraph line. If the mind is to know the meaning of the word, this information must also be transmitted by a similar neuronal process.

When I desire to make a written or spoken statement, the proper words are selected out of my memory storage and arranged by the Wernicke area of my brain in an order that conforms with stored rules of grammar, and then transmitted through the Broca area to the appropriate section of the motor cortex to activate the muscles for speech or writing. Before arriving at these muscles, the transmitted impulses are fine tuned by the cerebellum. The words constituting a sentence need not be actually spoken and yet the mind can still hear them as the impulses run through the neural systems.

If one were to assume that the mind knows nothing of a sentence until the very complex sequence of impulses that represent that sentence is passing through the brain, then one has difficulty describing how that sequence of impulses got started and organized to project the idea being addressed by the sentence before the idea exists. It appears reasonable to believe, therefore, that the mind has a dynamics that is independent, in some important respects, of the dynamics of the brain, and which can entertain a nonverbal conception of an idea and the desire to verbalize it. Often, on hearing the initial verbalization, the mind may reject it and call for another statement. It may repeat this process a number of times until it is satisfied that the words express the intended idea.

In normal conversation in which simple ideas are involved, the words pour forth at a great rate as if residing on the tip of the tongue without any apparent effort on word selection and order. In attempting to frame a complex idea, however, the mind may critically consider various word arrangements and may search the memory bank for the special word that provides the statement with the proper nuance. The holding of a nonverbal idea in the mind, the desire to verbalize it, and the process of judging the adequacy of a verbalization appear to involve purely mental dynamics.

When a person is reading or listening to a lengthy sentence, words representing a phrase of the sentence occupy the mind briefly and recede from the mind as the next phrase engages the mind. This process continues until the completion of the consideration of the sentence. At this time, in spite of the fact that the person's mind does not experience simultaneously all the words of the sentence, nevertheless it may experience the impression that it understands the statement. When asked for the meaning of the statement, the person does not give a verbatim replication of the sentence. Instead his words represent his understanding of the statement, and in choosing his words he takes into consideration his opinion of the listener's ability to understand. Understanding appears to be purely a mental phenomenon. And how the mind builds and retains understanding as words enter and recede from the mind is a mystery.

In the process of creative thinking, in which the mind is reaching for a new concept in, for example, science, philosophy, or art, the mind is in control as it probes various avenues of thought. The mind calls on the processes of the brain to provide appropriate words, images, and other stored content to support its operation.

It was previously pointed out that in ordinary conversation one is not aware of searching one's memory bank for words and engaging one's Wernicke area to arrange these words into grammatically correct sequence; but rather, one experiences these words in correct arrangement flowing quickly and effortlessly from one's lips. To explain this experience, it is suggested that the NOME representing mind is in immediate contact with many words in the memory bank and with many rules in the Wernicke area and, like a pianist with his fingers on many piano keys, this NOME produces the proper words in proper grammatical construction in concert to express the mind's intent. When a word is required with which the NOME is not in immediate contact, one notices a pause while the NOME searches the memory bank for the word that satisfies the mind. The NOME can, by the inflections it places on the vocalization of a given statement, endow it with emotional overtones of the mind's choice; for example, anger, fear, friendliness, and so forth. It can cancel the vocalization of a thought if the mind fears that the thought might offend the listener.

The sequences of ionic impulses that traverse the neural pathways of the visual systems when one sees a word and remembers it in the context of its meaning are entirely different from those which set the vocal cords into vibration and activate the other anatomical components in the subsequent vocalization of the word. They are also different from the sequences of impulses that move the hand in the writing of the word. In the writing of a statement involving familiar words, symbols flow from the tip of the pen with the facility that attends the speaking of the statement. It is conceivable that the translation of the ionic impulses relating to the recalled set of stored words into those relating to the speaking or writing of those words may be performed by the machinery of the brain. But the choice of the medium through which they are expressed, simply by willing it, is an operation of the mind.

The Role of Vis Mentis

Vis mentis, energy of mind, and its laws are not the NOME that embodies mind. The theory of vis mentis is proposed with the objective of introducing a representation of mind into the scientific view of nature as a matter-energy system. The worth of this concept will depend on its utility in systemizing, to the extent that systematization is possible, mental processes and their interactions with physical processes. Some elementary examples of the laws of vis mentis are given in the next chapter.

Chapter Nineteen

The Laws Relating
to Energy of Mind

The Limited Role of Mathematics

In the motion of inanimate bodies, like the orbiting of the planets around the sun, deterministic mathematical equations apply. With these equations one can compute with great precision the location of a given planet at a given time.

When one goes to the subatomic world, one finds that strict predictive determinism begins to disappear, and that the behavior of a particle is described by a mathematics that gives only a probability for finding a particle at a given place at a given time.

The laws of vis mentis relate to interactions between mind and body and to the dynamics of the flow of the subjective content of the mind. And in this domain the role of mathematics becomes even more tenuous. But it should be borne in mind that mathematics was invented by man to assist him in his reasoning processes. Nature does not utilize Newton's, Einstein's, or Maxwell's equations to assist in directing the movements of components. Nor does nature decree that there must be a mathematics, devisable by man, to describe in all its manifestations the performance of vis mentis.

Insight into the laws of vis mentis is still embryonic. Some laws are expressible in mathematical terms, others are expressible in the looser terminology of cause and effect statements, and others are stated as mental process descriptions. The objective of the present discussion is limited to presenting illustrations of these several classes of laws of vis mentis.

The Role of Subjective Data

In the final analysis all data are subjective in the sense that they result from one's translation of various neural pulse trains into mental experiences relevant to that data. Certain of these mental experiences are classified as objective data because they related to something that comes to one from the objective world—a world outside one's mind. Objective data are associated with sensory processes. The sight of a church, the sight of a man in rage, the sound of a church bell, the fragrance of a rose, and the like, are all considered to be objective data in spite of the fact there is no sound in the objective world; there are only the associated air vibrations; there is no odor in the objective world; there is only the associated emanation of certain molecules from the rose.

Subjective data relates to the total content of one's consciousness, the mental experiences of sensations, emotions, and thoughts. To a given person objective data are a subset of subjective data and one must learn to distinguish objectivity from fantasy. Objective data can be shared as data by many people. The vision of a church, the peal of the church bell, and so forth, represent shared data.

To the psychologist and psychiatrist the behavior of a patient and the stimuli impacting on the patient's sensory systems are taken as objective data. The patient's associated mental experiences which the psychologist and psychiatrist must infer from the patient's behavior or verbalization are called subjective data.

The psychologist and psychiatrist are concerned with the laws of vis mentis that relate mainly to the interactions between the objective state and the subjective state in any given patient and in people in general.

Philosophers identified as phenomenologists deal mainly with the laws relating to the dynamics of the flow of subjective experiences.

Some Mathematical Relationships

The relation of the intensities of the subjective experiences evoked by stimuli impacting on the sensory organs to the intensities of these stimuli appears to be describable in terms of conventional mathematics.

A person's subjective reaction to changes in light intensity, for example, is illustrative of such a process in vis mentis. A person is asked to look at a light of a certain intensity, which we will call the reference intensity. Then the intensity is increased in small steps, and between each incremental step the light of reference intensity is flashed for comparison. The person is asked to state when he can first discern a difference in intensity between the reference light and the light of increased intensity. Let us represent by a value A the ratio of the intensity of the augmented light to the reference intensity for the initial detection of a difference in intensity. On further experimentation at other values of reference intensity, it is found that the same value of A is obtained regardless of what reference intensity is used, provided that the intensity employed in the test is within the normal visual range of the person under test.

From this invariance in the value of A, one can derive mathematically the law that the intensity of one's subjective response to light varies as the logarithm of the intensity of the light source.

This relationship between subjective response and intensity of sensory stimulus is the Weber-Fechner law. It applies not only to light but also to the other sensory experiences. It is accurate over the normal range of sensory stimuli and becomes inaccurate at the extreme ends of the range.

The physico-psychic transduction of sensory system inputs into mental experiences is actually more complex than the foregoing discussion indicates. To account for the deviation of observed data from the Weber-Fechner law at low light intensities, R. L. Gregory suggests that the random pulses (called noise) in the neurons of the retina provide a contribution to the neural excitation produced by the imposed light intensity. Gregory shows that with the addition to the imposed light intensity of a constant representing the excitation contributed by the random pulses, he can obtain an improved agreement of the Weber-Fechner law with the test data.[1]

Further complications in the law relating the sensitivity of the mind to sensory inputs are observed when the senses are confronted with more complex signals than the simple intensity changes used in the initial derivation of the Weber-Fechner law. Some examples of these further complications are pointed out by S. A. Gelfand in his summarization of experimentation in the field of acoustics.[2] He discusses, for example, the sensitivity of the mind to such items as changes in sound frequency and beat signals produced by imposing simultaneously two signals of slightly different frequencies. These more complicated cases still fall in the domain of phenomena amenable to mathematical representation because systematic relations are obtained for the sensitivity of the mind to the inputs into the sensory systems.

On the Physico-Psychic Processes
Relating to the Weber-Fechner Law

The transduction of a signal impacting on a sensory organ into a mental experience may be considered as occurring in two stages: (1) the transduction of the input signal intensity into impulse rate in the neurons that detect, transmit, and process this input information; and (2) the transduction of the impulse rate in the neurons of the appropriate cerebral cortex into a mental experience.

The sensory receptor systems are sensitive to a tremendous range of stimuli. For example, the loudest sound tolerable to the ear has an intensity a trillion times that of the faintest detectable sound. Signal intensity is represented in neural transmission by the number of impulses per second. The neural impulse rate can vary over the range from 1 to 300 pulses per second (see chap. 7). Therefore it is reasonable to believe that the logarithmic translation occurs in the physical processing of the sensory stimuli into neural pulses rather than in the mental translation of pulse rate in the sensory cortex into a mental experience of signal intensity; the mental translation may be nearly linear.

This observation is born out by data obtained by H. K. Hartline on the pulse rates measured in the neuron of the eye of an invertebrate in response to four successive light flashes each one ten times more intense than its predecessor. The pulse rate differences can be shown to be proportional to the logarithm of the relative light intensities, indicating that the logarithmic translation occurs in the physical processing of the signal. The Hartline data are presented by Eccles[3] and by Granit;[4] the latter provides additional information in support of the logarithmic relation between the intensity of sensory input and the associated neural pulse rate.

Imprecise Laws of Vis Mentis

The more complex manifestations of vis mentis, for example, idea formulation, inspirational conceptualization, and volitive processes may never be describable in mathematical terms. Some of these complex manifestations of vis mentis may follow approximate rules. If, for example, one reveals one's religious, philosophic, or political ideology, to which one claims a strong adherence, then one can expect behavior that is related to this ideology. This behavior may manifest itself at a moment of opportunity. It is impossible to predict the timing and form of the behavioral manifestation. Nevertheless, we do have an approximate law to the effect that one's belief system does influence one's behavior.

A belief system is not simply a special setting of neuronal switches that automatically control a person's behavior in a prescribed way in response to a given stimulus. It is, instead, a set of consciously understood principles that can call for an infinite variety of responses to an infinite variety of stimuli.

Psychologists and psychiatrists delve into the domain of approximate law when they investigate the relation between a person's behavior and ideas—both the ideas expressed and the ideas stored in forgotten or forbidden recesses of the mind.[5] But to these investigators the mind of a person is more than an energy following certain laws; they view it, in essence, as a soul for whose well-being they are concerned.

Laws Relating to the Dynamics of the Stream of Consciousness

In contrast to the psychologists and psychiatrists, who assume the existence of the objective world, phenomenologists like Edmund Husserl, reject this assumption. Husserl holds that the only reality that one can accept with certainty is the content of one's mind and that any attempt to build a conception or science of the objective world must be grounded in the science of subjectivity.

Husserl points out that

> the universal sensuous experience in whose evidence the world is continuously given to us beforehand is obviously not to be taken forthwith as an apodictic evidence. . . . Not only can a particular experienced thing suffer devaluation as an illusion of the senses; the whole unitarily surveyable nexus, experienced throughout a period of time, can prove to be an illusion, a coherent dream.[6]

> Thus the being of the pure ego and his cogitations, as a being that is prior in itself, is antecedent to the natural being of the world.[7]

Husserl's approach to the study of the science of consciousness is, in effect, a study of vis mentis as an entity in itself, unbound by any influence of the laws that relate to the physical infrastructure that supports vis mentis. Illustrative of Husserl's observations on this science of consciousness are the following:

On time:

> If we consider the fundamental form of synthesis, namely iden-
> tification, we encounter it first of all as an all-ruling, passively
> flowing synthesis, in the form of the continuous conscious-
> ness of internal time. Every subjective process has its internal
> temporality.[8]

Time in the so-called objective world appears in the mind as the subjective experience of the positions of the hands of a clock. Internal and objective time do not track together. The clock hands move slowly when one is bored and move rapidly when one's mind is engaged in an interesting thought process.

On synthesis: Husserl reflects on a synthesis that operates as the various aspects of an object unfold with time and as they are experienced in various modes of consciousness,

> ... for example, in separate perceptions, recollections, expecta-
> tions, valuations and so forth. Again it is a synthesis that, as a
> unitary consciousness embracing these separated processes, gives
> rise to the consciousness of identity and thereby makes any
> knowing of identity possible.[9]

On potentialities:

> ... every actuality involves its potentialities, which are not
> empty possibilities, but rather possibilities intentionally pre-
> delineated in respect of content—namely in the actual subjective
> process itself—and in addition, having the character of pos-
> sibilities actualizable by the Ego.[10]

Husserl, expanding on the theme of potentialities, indicates that associated with each subjective state there are
horizons made up of "perceptions we could have had if we

actively directed the course of perception otherwise" and "explication" or unfolding of that conscious state which can take a large variety of directions. As the stream of consciousness flows in the course of approaching these horizons, new vistas are revealed exposing a new set of horizons. This stream of consciousness is synthesized into a unit representing the subjective experience under contemplation.

These few examples taken from Husserl's analysis indicate the thrust of his study of the science of consciousness.

Thought, as Husserl indicates, has the freedom to move in various directions probing the implications of new horizons as they come into view. Imagination, inspiration, and logic all can affect the flow of thought. Thinking is not a mechanistic process amenable to mathematical description. Coherent with the movement of thought there is the related dynamics of vis mentis; the two are intimately associated. Vis mentis, a component of the matter-energy system of nature, can affect other components of the system. A related thought is expressed by Sperry:

> The events of inner experiences, as emergent properties of the brain processes, become themselves explanatory causal constructs in their own right, interacting at their own level with their own laws and dynamics. The world of inner experience . . . long rejected by 20th century scientific materialism, becomes recognized and included within the domain of science.[11]

The summarization of the present knowledge on the laws of vis mentis would be a major undertaking, one I have not attempted to pursue. My purpose in this discussion is to indicate some of the facets of this subject.

On the Concepts of Vis Mentis and Soul

The vis mentis and soul concepts are similar to the extent that both provide for some control by the mind over processes of the body. There are, however, important differences between the two concepts.

1. Vis mentis and the mind it represents are components of nature. The soul is a supernatural entity.

2. Vis mentis arose in living organisms when structures evolved capable of transforming electrical energy into energy of mind. This theory allows for the occurrence of mental events not only in humans but also in some lesser species like dogs, horses, and the like. The soul, which is the home of mental events, is instilled by God only into human bodies.

3. Vis mentis follows certain laws and in some of its manifestations is measurable (e.g., the Weber-Fechner law). The soul, being a supernatural entity, is not measurable nor is it bound by law.

4. The mind in the vis mentis theory experiences fatigue when the electrical energy that transforms into energy of mind is depleted. The soul, which is not tied to physical energies, should suffer no reduction in its general sense of being during fatigue of the body.

5. The vis mentis of a given person may disappear when the physical processes that produce it cease. Concerning the soul after death of the body, Descartes believed: "The human body may easily perish, but . . . the mind or soul of man, between which I find no distinction, is immortal by its very nature." [13]

Although Penfield posits a naturalistic origin for the energy of mind, nevertheless he suggests that this energy may survive the death of a person sustained by energy provided by God. The survival of energy as an independent entity occurs in the world of the physicist. For example, a photon, produced when an electron in an atom jumps from its orbit to an orbit in which its energy is lower, will survive as a quantum of electromagnetic energy until it experiences a special encounter with a particle of matter.

Penfield, I believe, viewed energy of mind as the actual essence of subjectivity. In the vis mentis theory, vis mentis and its laws, as part of the matter-energy conception of nature, is a scheme for dealing with the subjective aspect of nature. We do not understand the being of the subjective and the objective aspects of nature in the absolute. Nor do we know whether there are realms of being other than those that can impinge on our neural systems. With so limited an understanding, it would be foolhardy to take a dogmatic position on the survival of one's mental essence after the death of one's body.

Chapter Twenty

Some Philosophical Considerations

My objective is to discuss the brain-mind relation in the light of modern neurological insight into the structure and processes of the brain. In consonance with this objective, the assumption is made that a person is structured as described by the neuroscientist and physiologist. I call this assumption the "anatomical premise."

A person, according to the anatomical premise, is equipped with sensory organs, that is, eyes, ears, and the like, which, when impacted by signals from the objective world, send streams of ionic impulses through nerve systems to the brain. There, by some incredible legerdemain, nature transmutes these streams of ionic impulses into mental experiences of pictures, sounds, odors, and other sensory modalities, and excites related thoughts and emotions. The person is aware of these mental experiences, and not of the associated streams of ionic impulses.

I will not attempt to review the extensive literature on the brain-mind (also called the body-mind) relations. An appraisal of this literature is given by Shaffer in his book *Philosophy of Mind.*[1] I will limit my discussion to a number of topics having some relevance to the thesis of this book.

I will comment, only in passing, on radical idealism, behaviorism, a radical materialistic concept, and epiphenomenalism.

According to Berkeley, one of the principals of radical idealism, all those bodies which compose the mighty frame of the world, have not any substance without a mind, that their "being" is to be perceived or known; consequently as long as they are not actually perceived by me or do not exist in any mind, or that of any other created spirit, they either must have no existence at all, or else subsist in the mind of some Eternal Spirit.[2]

If Berkeley seems to accept the idea that he is endowed with eyes and other sensory organs when he says: "By sight I have ideas of light and color. . . . By touch I perceive hard and soft," he would have difficulty providing a convincing rationale for the need of these organs that are structured to respond to signals from the objective world.

Psychologists John Watson and B. F. Skinner, and philosopher J. J. C. Smart, among others, advocate a concept of radical materialism, called behaviorism. They hold that the objective world and its behavior are the only realities. Watson, for example, says: "Belief in the existence of consciousness goes back to the ancient days of superstition and magic." In a related vein, Smart writes:

> A man is a vast arrangement of physical particles, but there is not, over and above this, sensations or states of consciousness. There are just behavioral facts about this vast mechanism.[3]

The behaviorist accepts the anatomical premise. According to this premise, the "behavioral facts" relating to the "vast mechanism" of the behaviorist's brain are that inputs from the objective world are received and processed as ionic impulses. But the behaviorist is aware of this information only in terms of mental experiences. It is strange that the behaviorist closes his mind to this fact, and persistently advocates the notion that mental experiences are myths.

Epiphenomenalists, such as philosophers George Santayana and T. H. Huxley and neuroscientists Thatcher and John, accept the reality of both the mental and physical worlds, but hold that mental experiences are by-products of the physical processes of the brain, and cannot affect these processes. This concept is also called "one-substance dualism" to distinguish it from the two-substance concept of classical dualism.

Epiphenomenalists accept the anatomical premise, and would probably endorse Thatcher and John's hyperneuron theory. My criticisms of the hyperneuron theory, which apply also to all epiphenomenalistic theories, are given in chapter 16.

The Concept of Natural Dualism

The concept of the mind-body relationship, which I advocate in this book, I call "natural dualism." In chapter 6 I point out that the scientific description of nature implies the existence of two realms of being, namely a material realm and a nonmaterial realm. In the material realm lie the material objects of nature, while in the nonmaterial realm lie the NOMEs (e.g., gravitational and electrical) that move these objects. The interactions between these two realms are bilateral; for example, the spatial distribution of masses in the material realm determines the configuration of the gravitational field in the nonmaterial realm, which, in turn, influences the acceleration of the masses in the material realm. A similar bilateral interaction occurs between charged particles and the electrical NOME.

The NOMEs, as such, are not perceived; their existence and laws of interaction are inferred from the observed behavior of the material objects. How these laws are embedded in the nonmaterial realm and how they are implemented by nature is not understood. For computational and analytical purposes these NOMEs are represented in science by mathematical equations that define electrical and gravitational fields and specify their interactions with matter.

Whereas the body is generally viewed as existing in the

material realm, I have pointed out in chapter 6 that spatially it lies in both realms. Only one-trillionth of the body is occupied by matter. The rest of the body is occupied by an electric field, which holds the atoms of the body in place to give it shape and strength, and which mediates most of its processes.

In consonance with this dualistic view of nature, I propose that consciousness with its content of mental experiences is an exciter in nature's nonmaterial realm. As in the case of the mechanistic NOMEs, a bilateral interaction exists between consciousness and the material realm. Objects in the material realm, through the agency of the body's sensory organs and neural systems, generate pictures, sounds, odors, and other sensory modalities in the NOME of consciousness, where they might stimulate thoughts and emotions. Conversely, in response to its content of sensations, thoughts, and emotions, the NOME representing consciousness may move objects in the material realm employing the brain and the body as its agents. Consciousness shares with the mechanistic NOMEs the mystery concerning its mode of existence and operation.

Classical dualism, according to which the soul was instilled into the human body by God, also posits a bilateral interaction between the mind and the body. According to natural dualism, consciousness arose in living organisms when the necessary physical structures evolved. This theory allows for the existence of some aspects of consciousness in less highly developed species than man.

The Incredible Domain of the Mind

The mental NOME is the home of sensations, emotions, and thoughts. In the brain there are only movements of ions and chemicals. And in the world outside the brain there are only physical entities like photons, airwaves, and special molecules that can impact on the eyes, ears, and nose respectively. There was, for example, no light in the universe until the advent of a mind that could experience light.

The mind develops a concept of time and space. It places immediate experiences in the present, recollections in the past, and expectations in the future. The mind learns to order objects in terms of size and distance between them. The mental NOME exists in association with the body and moves with it in the space-time world.

Although the mind depends for its energy on brain processes, it develops a unique dynamics that transcends these processes. It develops understanding of statements and concepts, and this understanding persists after the words that structure it have passed as ionic impulses through the machinery of the brain. The mind can call up words to clothe a concept it yearns to express in a great variety of combinations. The words may change but the concept expressed remains invariant. This yearning to express an idea exists in the mind prior to the clothing of the idea with words, and the mind critiques, rejects, and accepts words until it feels that the desired idea is properly expressed.

The Central State Identity Theory

The central state identity theory is currently one of the most seriously discussed mind-body ideas. In this theory mental state terms are identified with complex neurological states in the brain. When a complex neurological state identified by a mental state term causes a subsequent neurological state which has associated with it another mental state term, then one might say, in a manner of speaking, that a mental event has caused another mental event. And if that second neurological state causes neural activity that stimulates body movements, one might say that a mental state has caused a physical act.

Because the mental state terms in this theory are merely

names for complex physical states and nothing more, the central state identity theory is a radical materialistic theory. It fails to take account of the miracle of the existence of the subjective states as personal experiences. It implies that one neurological state can induce a second significant neurological state without any impact of the meanings that these states have to the person involved. This is a rash assumption in the face of one's observation that the meanings in one's subjective experiences are powerful motivating forces in one's life.

Proponents of the central state identity theory are philosophers U. T. Place, J. J. C. Smart, and Herbert Feigl.

Functionalism

The proponents of functionalism, a mind-body theory of current vintage, claim that this theory avoids the objections raised against dualism on the one hand and materialism on the other.

Functionalists, such as Jerry A. Fodor, acknowledge the existence of mental states but hold that we have no basis for assuming that only things that have organic neural systems can have mental states. According to Fodor:

> Functionalism recognizes the possibility that systems as diverse as human beings, calculating machines, and disembodied spirits could all have mental states.[4]

Functionalists posit that if a thing has a complex of internal states that can interact and thereby affect the output of that thing in its response to an input, then that thing may have mental states. Fodor illustrates this proposition with his description of a coke vending machine. The machine has two internal states designated S1 and S2. The machine is so designed that if it is in state S1, and if one inserts a dime the machine dispenses a coke and remains in state S1. If subsequently a nickel is inserted the machine goes into state S2 and does not dispense a coke. Then if a nickel is inserted the machine dispenses a coke and goes to state S1, or, if a dime is inserted, the machine dispenses a coke and a nickel and goes into state S1. This machine, according to functionalism, may have mental states.

Engineers frequently design electrical and mechanical equipment that have the relation between internal states and input-output performance described by Fodor. But these internal states are all physical. The science relating to the design and operation of this equipment contains no information concerning the physico-psychic transduction process whereby physical states can induce mental states. There is no evidence that this remarkable process has ever been built into a machine either by intent or chance. Thus the thesis that man-made mechanical or electrical devices may experience mental states is gratuitous speculation. This kind of speculation could lead one to claim with equal authority that the kitchen table has mentally composed a symphony.

Fodor admits concern about the ability of functionalism to deal adequately with mental states, which he calls "qualitative content":

> Many psychologists who are inclined to accept the functionalist framework are nevertheless worried about the failure of functionalism to reveal much about the nature of consciousness. . . . As matters stand, the problem of qualitative content poses a serious threat to the assertion that functionalism can provide a general theory of the mental.[5]

Double Aspect Theory

According to the double aspect theory, a person should be viewed not as consisting of two entities—a body and a mind—but instead as a single entity having both physical and mental attributes. P. F. Strawson attempts to defend this theory by philosophical discourse. He states:

What I mean by the concept of a person is the type of entity such that both predicates ascribing states of consciousness and predicates ascribing corporial characteristics, a physical situation, etc. are equally applicable to a single individual of that single type.[6]

But Strawson does not explain how the flow of the physical and mental manifestations of a person manage to bear a meaningful relation to each other in time.

Interactions

Because the mechanism for the interaction between physical and mental events cannot be explained, philosophers tend to seek theories that avoid the problem of this interaction. Behaviorists reject the reality of mind. Idealists hold that the mind rather than the physical world is the true reality. Epiphenomenalists believe that mental events cannot influence brain processes.

The lack of understanding of the interaction process should not be a factor in the choice of a mind-body theory. As I have pointed out in chapter 6, even interactions between material objects are mysterious. They are mediated by NOMEs. The mind is also a NOME.

Panpsychic Implications

All atoms contain electrons and protons that are endowed with electric fields. If one holds with Thatcher and John that the electric field is the stuff with which mind is related, then one has a physical basis for belief in panpsychic concept of the universe.

Panpsychic concepts of the universe were held by many philosophers and scientists, among whom are G. T. Fechner, Josiah Royce, Herman Lotze, G. W. Leibniz, Arthur Schopenhauer, Baruch Spinosa, A. N. Whitehead, and Pierre Teilhard de Chardin. Royce, for example, says "Where we see inorganic nature seemingly dead, there is in fact, conscious life, just as surely as there is Being present in Nature at all."[7] Panpsychists hold that it is absurd to think that, as atoms joined to form molecules and molecules joined to form complex structures which eventually evolved into living things, at some point in this process a new essence called mind entered into these structures. They feel that it is more reasonable to believe that the essence called mind exists in the elementary particles and attains higher realms of mentality as the structures evolve to more complex forms. Thatcher and John concur:

> The difference between a human being and an elementary particle becomes an enormous quantitative difference in the number of energy states which can be entered, but a qualitative continuum can be postulated.[8]

In carefully controlled scientific experiments it is found that inanimate objects faithfully follow mechanistic laws. There is no scientific evidence regarding the existence of mind in these objects. Neither is it possible to experience directly the mental states in these objects. In the absence of any supportive evidence the verity of panpsychism remains unresolved.

The vis mentis theory of consciousness allows, as a possibility, a nonpanpsychic thesis for the genesis of consciousness. This theory posits the existence of a very special structure in living things capable of transforming electrical energy into energy of mind. Possibly consciousness appeared in nature when in the course of development of living organisms this special energy transforming physical structure evolved.

Part Seven

Epilogue

Chapter Twenty-One

The Nonmaterial
Realm of Nature

The view advanced in this book that nature consists of material objects and of nonmaterial exciters (NOMEs) that activate these objects induces speculations on the potentialities of NOMEs. No brief is made for the thoughts presented in this chapter, some of which must be viewed as merely interesting flights of fancy.

At the time of the "big-bang" when the universe had disintegrated into a sea of fundamental particles, there also existed NOMEs that in time formed this debris into atoms, molecules, suns, planets, and eventually into living organisms.

The most complex in structure and function of the living organisms that had been created on earth is *Homo sapiens*. Members of this species are endowed with a NOME called consciousness, which has the capability to transduce physical processes into mental events. It is in terms of these nonmaterial mental events that members of this species perceive the universe and wonder about it.

Human perception of a material object is implemented primarily by light waves, which emerge from or are reflected by the object, and which impact on the neurons on the retina of the eye. This impact initiates electrical impulses in these neurons, which, following neural pathways to and through the brain, are eventually transduced into a mental experience of a picture representing the object. One has a direct knowledge of the picture as a mental experience. One derives no information from this experience regarding the structure of the light that impacted the eye. The light wave consists of an assembly of photons. Each photon is a quantum of vibratory electromagnetic energy, a NOME which, as such, is hidden from human perception.

The light visible to man is only a small portion of the spectrum of the electromagnetic wave phenomena in nature. At the high energy end of this spectrum are gamma rays which were discovered in the twentieth century when scientists invented instruments that could detect their presence. Before the invention of these instruments, a person subjected to irradiation by gamma rays may suffer physical damage that may lead to early death, and yet during the irradiation incident may have felt nothing from the then undetectable rays.

One is struck with the thought that there may exist in nature other NOMEs, as yet undetected because of the lack of the necessary instruments. And these exciters may be having subtle influences on people and other material things in nature which escape current recognition.

An as yet undiscovered NOME may be involved in some aspects of information transmittal. This speculative thought is suggested by the following considerations. From the time of its formation four-and-a-half billion years ago, the earth has been impacted by radio waves bearing information concerning the nature of distant astronomical bodies. With the development of the necessary radio receivers in the twentieth century, scientists first became aware of the existence of this stream of information. Scientists are now analyzing these data for information that may have been sent by intelligent extraterrestrial beings. However, these beings may be utilizing a NOME that has not yet been discovered by humans.

Possibly the human brain, properly sensitized and tuned, may be beginning to receive signals through this posited NOME. Inspired thoughts that suddenly and unexpectedly flash in the mind may be coming through this NOME. Possibly this NOME may mediate the phenomenon of mental telepathy. And the transmittal speed of information by means of this NOME may not be limited to the speed of light as are radio waves.

Parapsychologists claim that mental telepathy is a reality, but many scientists question the validity of their data. If irrefutable data in support of mental telepathy is obtained, then it may be necessary to accept this posited NOME as the mediator of this phenomenon.

Bell's theorem derived (1964) by physicist J. S. Bell from the theory of quantum mechanics lends support to the idea that information may be transmitted at a speed greater than the speed of light. The question of the speed of transmission of information arises in the following thought experiment, which is of a type suggested by Einstein (in collaboration with B. Podolsky and N. Rosen).

Imagine two identical subatomic particles which had been joined and which are now separated. These particles differ only in that one has a spin around its up axis and the other has its spin around its down axis. Imagine further that these particles are removed from each other by an immense distance. Bell's theorem predicts that if one of these particles were rotated by a magnetic field to spin about its right axis, then instantaneously the other particle would spin about its left axis.

Einstein argued that this prediction of the transmission of information at a speed greater than the speed of light is evidence that the theory of quantum mechanics is flawed. However, because quantum mechanics has proven to give correct predictions in every case to which it was applied, many physicists now believe that its prediction of transmission speeds greater than light is correct.

The electrical and gravitational NOMEs posited in physical science are depicted graphically as imaginary equipotential surfaces representing fields of electrical and gravitational potential energy respectively. These representations show the sources of the fields and the distribution of their energies and, in conjunction with the associated mathematical equations, permit the calculation of the effects of the associated NOMEs on physical objects. As emphasized many times previously, these fields and equations are not the NOME itself, but represent the physicist's scheme for dealing with the influences of the NOME.

I have added the energy of mind, vis mentis, and its laws to this system in order to bring into the science of nature the phenomena of mind. Vis mentis and its laws are not the NOME, mind, but are useful surrogates for this NOME.

Where the field of the mind is located in the body of a person is a matter of pure conjecture. I offer the following thoughts to provoke consideration of this subject. I suggest that the roots of the mind field lie in the upper brain stem, specifically in the thalamus, because any intrusion into this area causes loss of consciousness. In contrast the excising of a large portion of one's neocortex does not extinguish consciousness. I further suggest that the mind field extends to special cortices in the brain involved in brain-mind interactions. It also extends to peripheral areas of the body, possibly following the nervous systems. This last suggestion is based on the fact that although an infected tooth sends its information to the brain, the pain is felt not in the brain but in the vicinity of the tooth. Similarly the pain generated by a bruised toe is a mental experience at the toe.

The Darwinian theory of evolution holds that *Homo sapiens* evolved mechanistically through a process involving chance mutations in the genetic molecule in the seeds of species, and the natural selection of those progenies best able to survive. There is no need to dwell on the details of this well-known process. But it should be remarked that the genetic molecule is more than the blueprint of the associated organism; it is also the factory.

The genetic molecule in man, for example, fabricates an

amazing variety of very complex molecules out of material supplied from the environment and assembles them to produce bones, muscles, tendons, skin, arteries, blood, nerves, brain, glands, viscera, and other components, all properly interconnected to form a living structure. This structure is endowed with the ability to grow and to heal many of its injuries. It is provided with the capabilities to seek food, to protect itself, to reproduce its kind, to perceive the world in terms of mental experiences, to establish emotional ties with other living creatures, and to create theories about what it perceives.

Electrical energy and its laws represent the NOME that, according to physical science, binds atoms together to form molecules, and is involved in their interactions. Scientists can readily understand how a small crystal immersed in an environment that contains atoms of its kind can, employing this NOME, capture atoms that impact on it and incorporate them into its orderly crystallographic structure. It is readily conceivable that this NOME is the active agent in the replication of various portions of the genetic molecule to provide the many different kinds of molecules that are the building blocks of the structure of the body.

Scientists, however, have no understanding of how these molecules are moved and joined to form the many components of the human body in proper composition, shape, size, and association, according to the plan encoded in the genetic molecule. This understanding is lacking even in the case of a single-celled bacterium. The properties of electric fields are well known and these fields are not sufficiently complex to decode the genetic plan and execute it. One is tempted to infer that a much more capable NOME associated with the human genetic molecule carries and implements the plan, and that this NOME has a seed of consciousness which it instills into the body it constructs. This consciousness then grows as the bodily processes provide energy and information.

Several billion years ago certain molecules, which were precursors of living organisms, were formed when their component atoms met by chance under the proper environmental conditions and joined. These molecules eventually united to form primitive living organisms and their genetic molecules. What strange alchemy endowed these genetic molecules with the capability to encode the structural plans of these living organisms, to construct such organisms, and to generate, through accidental changes in these genetic molecules, mutations in the associated species? This process of generating mutations, and the process of survival of the fittest eventually brought into being the human species. By some incredible legerdemain the genetic molecules of the human species endow members of this species with the gift of consciousness. Scientists cannot explain the cited feats of alchemy and legerdemain whereby microscopic assemblies of atoms attained such extraordinary powers.

Man is a component of nature, and his processes are natural. When a man thinks, then and there nature is thinking. For at least the last century, men have, through selective breeding and genetic engineering, directed the evolution of plants and animals toward forms that serve man's purposes. Did nature have to develop human beings by chance processes before thought and purpose could enter the evolutionary process? The magnificence of the genetic molecule as an engineering feat leads one to suspect that the capability for purposeful thought existed from the beginning as a sovereign, concerned NOME with majestic abilities.

Eastern mystics and some physicists, like Capra and Bohm, believe that all things and all minds are conjoined in a "oneness." If this theory were correct, one would expect that all people would have the most exalted of thoughts as mediated by this "oneness." One finds, however, that people project a spectrum of thoughts ranging from debasing, murderous thoughts to sublime thoughts, and these thoughts can influence the behavior of the thinker. These considerations suggest that each person possesses his or her individual NOME, which is that person's private domain of consciousness and thought.

What happens to the NOME in which a given person's "selfhood" is embedded? The NOME mediating the mental activity of a person during life may disengage and neutralize at the time of that person's death, and that person's mind may have no further being. Or, on the death of the person, the person's NOME may retain some aspects of the person's individuality and may possess capabilities of a kind beyond human conception.

As pointed out in chapter 19, there is in physical science a precedent for the detachment of a NOME from a physical object whose processes generated that NOME, and for the subsequent existence of that NOME as a discrete entity. When an electron jumps from its orbit in an atom to an orbit in which its total energy is decreased, a photon, a quantum of electromagnetic energy is created, and the energy of this photon is equal to the energy lost by the electron. This photon is a NOME and, if it does not encounter a particle with which it interacts, it can endure until the end of time without losing its individuality.

Similarly, in a given person the Self, a NOME, is created when, according to the vis mentis theory, a structure has formed in that person capable of bringing it into being. This Self subsequently grows in capability, fashioned by its experiences and by its aspirations. In the concept under present discussion it is supposed that at the death of the person this NOME is released into the nonmaterial domain of nature as a discrete entity. According to this supposition, nature, through naturalistic processes, creates Souls to eventually populate its nonmaterial domain.

In the absence of definitive evidence regarding the creation and eventual fate of the human Self, various theories have been proposed. These theories range from the rejection of the existence of Self to the creation of Self as a Soul by God. The present speculations delineate an additional possibility.

The volumes of all atomic assemblies that constitute the structures of the animate and the inanimate objects in the universe are occupied mainly by NOMEs (represented in science by the energy fields and their laws); the material substance of these objects occupies less than one-trillionth of their volumes, the remainder of the space is occupied by a NOME (see chap. 6). The NOME holds the atoms of these objects in place providing them with shape, structure, and strength, and it mediates their internal processes and their reactions to the impact of their environment. If, as previously speculated, all NOMEs are special manifestations of a single grand NOME then, all the entities of the universe, the animate (including their mental events) as well as the inanimate, are united in a "oneness."

It is not the intent in this book to delve into religious matters. However, one is moved to reflect that the idea of a grand NOME, with its awesome creative capabilities, which, for example, endowed humans with minds and with the ability to direct their own destinies, to struggle for survival, and yet to generate as they grew in mental experience, ideals of morality and compassion, leads one, through science, to a concept of God.

The emotion of understanding is experienced when one can find a consistent or logical connection between a newly observed phenomenon or a new thought and concepts which one has accepted as true, even though deeper analysis reveals that one does not really understand the accepted concepts. Language helps promote the illusion of understanding. We invent expressions like gravitational force and electrical force and are satisfied with explanations that employ these expressions in a logical way although we have no true understanding of what these forces are. Words are assembled to formulate ideas that are then designated by new words, like entropy and resonance. And these words become the basis for additional words. Thus we build a pyramid of words on which our understanding rests. A new conception of nature may alter the words at the base of the pyramid causing it to collapse and to be replaced by a new pyramid.

We now have a science of nature based on the current pyramid of words, whose primary virtue is that it is operationally useful, that is, it allows us to predict the course of observed phenomena. With the same operational intent, I have added to this pyramid the words vis mentis and its laws. But I recognize that a totally new conception of nature, which is bound to come, will provide a new pyramid of words that may serve as the basis for greater human insights.

Chapter Twenty-Two

The Human Psyche

Practice Supports the Potent Mind Theory

In the course of intellectual disputation, some people may hold that the mind can exercise some control over the body, others may hold that the mind is an impotent by-product of the physical process of the brain, and still others may hold that mind is a myth and that only behavior is real.

But regardless of their professed beliefs, all these people, even the epiphenomenologists and behaviorists, in directing their personal lives, and in their relations with other people, plan, act, and emote as if they believe that they are sensitive autonomous beings with some control over their destinies. In other words, in practice, all people behave as if they tacitly believe in the potency of their minds as projected by the vis mentis theory of consciousness rather than in the impotency view projected by the mechanistic theory.

The Testimony of Literature

In an incredible outpouring of songs, poems, stories, and essays, the human psyche reveals its inspirations, its traumas, its longings and its strivings in its great concern over "I" and "thee" as free spirits. Shakespeare wrote:

> When, in disgrace with fortune and men's eyes,
> I all alone beweep my outcast state,
> And trouble deaf heaven with my bootless cries,
> And look upon myself, and curse my fate,
> Wishing me like to one more rich in hope,

Featured like him, like him with friends possess'd,
Desiring this man's art and that man's scope,
With what I most enjoy contented least;
Yet in these thoughts myself almost despising,
Haply I think on thee, and then my state,
Like to the lark at break of day arising
From sullen earth, sings hymns at heaven's gate;
    For thy sweet love remember'd such wealth brings
    That then I scorn to change my state with kings.
                    —Sonnet XXIX

The Thrust of Self

From one's earliest recollections one is aware of a "self," a unified psyche within one's body, that fears, loves, hungers, and desires. This psyche establishes bonds of affection and love with other persons. It communicates with the others to exchange information or embark on a common venture. It seeks guidance from others. It consoles and helps others. This psyche, the "I," is proud of its physical and mental capabilities. It tries to correct its deficiencies in these areas by arduous practice and by learning.

"I" views with dismay deterioration of its mental and physical capabilities through disease or aging and takes measures to counter these trends. "I" is fearful of its ultimate demise. It mourns the death of a beloved as a soul departed.

"I" strives to comprehend, by mathematics and by whatever other process it can devise, the wonders it beholds in the universe. In this endeavor, "I" moves forward into an expanding horizon of thought, as it probes the infinitude of space and time. "I" looks toward heaven for a hint of its purpose and destiny, a justification for its agonies. "I" finds solace in belief.

So I walk on uplands unbounded, and know that there is hope, for that which thou dist mold out of dust to have consort with things eternal.[1]

On the Being of the Psyche

What mode of being can we assign to the human psyche, the "I"? In chapter 1, I point out that in the purely physical domain we are directly aware of material objects and their movements and attribute reality to these objects and their movements. From the movements of these objects we infer the existence of a class of entities that causes them, which are represented by scientists as electrical and gravitational forces and their respective laws. Although we do not know how these forces are imbedded in nature or how they take hold of objects and move them in accordance with their laws, nevertheless we believe that they exist.

From observations of the remarkable performance of humans and from my introspective view of the drama of my subjective experiences, I infer the existence of the human psyche. I classify this psyche as a NOME. As in the case of the NOMEs of physical science, I do not know how this NOME of psyche is imbedded in nature nor how it manages to interact with the brain with which it is associated; nevertheless I attribute to it at least the same level of reality that I assign to the NOMEs of physical science. It is only through the proper operation of this psychic NOME, namely, its translation of neural impulses into mental experiences, that I know of the existence of physical objects and the influences of their NOMEs. In short, to the extent that I can know reality, I believe in the reality of the human psyche.

Notes

Chapter 1: Introduction

1. Alexander Dyce, *The Works of Richard Bentley* (London, 1938), 3:21.

2. Norman Cousins, *Human Options* (New York: W. W. Norton & Co., 1981), 24.

Chapter 2: On the Mental and Physical Worlds and Reality

1. Robert W. Thatcher and E. Roy John, *Functional Neuroscience: Volume 1: Foundations of Cognitive Processes* (Hillside, N.J.: Lawrence Erlbaum, 1977), 249.

2. Julian Jaynes, *The Origin of Consciousness in the Breakdown of the Bicameral Mind* (Boston: Houghton-Mifflin Co., 1976), 75.

3. William James, *The Principles of Psychology* (New York: Dover Publications, 1958), 297–298.

4. Ibid., 341.

5. Ibid., 369.

6. Ibid., 348.

7. Ibid., 350.

8. Werner Heisenberg, *The Physicist's Conception of Nature,* trans. Arnold J. Pomarans (New York: Harcourt Brace and Co., 1958), 29.

9. David Shapiro, "A Biofeedback Strategy in the Study of Consciousness," in *Alternate States of Consciousness,* edited by Norman E. Zinberg, New York: Free Press, 1977, 146.

10. Robert E. Ornstein, *The Psychology of Consciousness* (New York: The Viking Press, 1972).

11. Charles T. Tart, *States of Consciousness* (New York: E. P. Dutton, 1975).

12. Fritjof Capra, *The Tao of Physics* (New York: Bantam Books, 1975), 5.

13. David Bohm, *Wholeness and the Implicate Order* (London: Routledge & Kegan Paul, 1980).

14. Marilyn Ferguson, *The Aquarian Conspiracy: Personal and Social Transformations in the 1980s* (Los Angeles: J. P. Tarcher, Inc., 1980).

Chapter 3: On The Scientific Method

1. Max Born, *Einstein's Theory of Relativity* (New York: Dover Publications, Inc., 1962), 334.

Chapter 4: The Enigma of Matter

1. John Locke, *An Essay on Human Understanding* (first published 1690).

2. Born, *Einstein's Theory of Relativity*, 33.

3. Werner Heisenberg, *The Physicist's Conception of Nature*, 29.

Chapter 5: Limits in the Scientific Understanding of Energy

1. From letters of Newton to Richard Bentley, 1692–1693, as quoted in notes of Cajori Edition of Newton (1697), 543. See *Gravitation* by C. W. Misner, K. S. Thorne, and John A. Wheeler (San Francisco: W. H. Freeman and Co., 1970), 40–41.

2. Max Jammer, *Concepts of Force* (Cambridge: Harvard University Press, 1957), 229.

Chapter 6: A Basic Mystery

1. Jammer, *Concepts of Force*, 257, 258, 261.

2. James Jeans, *The Mysterious Universe*, 146.

3. Stephen W. Hawking, *A Brief History of Time from the Big Bang Theory to Black Holes* (New York: Bantam Books, 1988), 9.

4. Rupert Sheldrake, *A New Science of Life* (Los Angeles: J. P. Tarcher, 1981), 71, 72.

5. Sheldrake, *The Presence of the Past: Morphic Resonance and the Habits of Nature* (New York: Times Books, 1988), 17.

6. Ibid., 18.

7. Ernest Gardner, *Fundamentals of Neurology* (Philadelphia: W. B. Saunders, 1915), 427.

8. Sheldrake, *The Presence of the Past,* 13.

9. Ibid., 177.

Chapter 7: Neural Structure and Processes

1. For further information the reader is referred to the following: Gardner, *Fundamentals of Neurology,* Thatcher and John, *Functional Neuroscience,* Wilder Penfield, *The Mystery of the Mind* (Princeton: Princeton University Press, 1975); Dean E. Wooldridge, *The Machinery of the Brain* (New York: McGraw-Hill, 1963); John C. Eccles, *The Understanding of the Brain* (New York: McGraw-Hill, 1963); and *Scientific American* 241 no. 3 (September 1979).

2. Pierre Morrell and William T. Norton, "Myelin," *Scientific American* 242, no. 5 (May 1980): 88–118.

3. Eric R. Kandel, "Small Systems of Neurons," *Scientific American* (September 1979): 74–75.

4. See Thatcher and John, *Functional Neuroscience,* 2, for a more complete discussion.

Chapter 8: Some Brain Components

1. Eccles, *The Understanding of the Brain,* 3.

2. Paul D. MacLean, *A Triune Concept of the Brain and Behavior* (Toronto: University of Toronto Press), 1973.

3. Carl Sagan, *The Dragons of Eden: Speculations on the Evaluation of Human Intelligence* (New York: Random House, 1977).

4. Penfield, *The Mystery of the Mind,* 18.

5. Thatcher and John, *Functional Neuroscience.*

6. Norman Geschwind, "Specializations of the Human Brain," *Scientific American* (September 1979): 182.

7. R. W. Sperry, "Hemisphere Disconnection and Unity in Conscious Awareness," *American Psychologist* 23 (October 1968): 723–733.

8. Eccles, *Understanding of the Brain,* 209–222.

9. Ornstein, *The Psychology of Consciousness.*

10. Penfield, *The Mystery of the Mind,* 16.

11. Ibid., 18.

12. Thatcher and John, *Functional Neuroscience,* 13.

13. Ibid., 17, 18.

Chapter 9: On Sensory Inputs to the Brain

1. Gardner, *Fundamentals of Neurology,* 246–267; Thatcher and John, *Functional Neuroscience,* 17, 136–153; David H. Hubel and Torsten N. Weisel, "Brain Mechanisms of Vision," *Scientific American* (September 1979): 150–162; A. R. Luria, *The Working Brain* (Middlesex: Penguin Press, 1973). (See Thatcher and John, 139.); Ivan Bodis-Wollner, Adam Atkin, Edward Raab, and Murray Wolkstein, "Visual Associations: Cortex and Vision in Man: Pattern Evoked Occipital Potentials in a Blind Boy," 198, no. 4317 *Science* (November 11, 1977): 629–630.

2. Thatcher and John, *Functional Neuroscience,* 135.

3. Stanley A. Gelfand, *Hearing: An Introduction to Psychological and Physiological Acoustics* (New York: Marcel Dekker, Inc., 1981), 162–171; A. J. Hudspeth, "The Cellular Basis of Hearing: The Biophysics of Hair Cells," 230, no. 4727 *Science* (November 15, 1985): 745–752; Thatcher and John, *Functional Neuroscience,* 139; Geschwind, "Specializations of the Human Brain," 190; Ragnar Granit, *Receptors and Sensory Perception,* (New Haven: Yale University Press, 1955), 299–301.

Chapter 10: Some Brain System Characteristics

1. Thatcher and John, *Functional Neuroscience,* 249.

2. Ibid., 219.

3. Ibid., 220.

4. Wooldridge, *The Machinery of the Brain,* 140.

5. R. Hernandez-Peon, H. Scherrer, and M. Jouvet, "Modification of Electrical Activity in Cochlear Nucleus During 'Attention' in Unaesthetized Cats." *Science* 123 (1956): 331–332.

6. Thatcher and John, *Functional Neuroscience,* 189.

7. Eccles, *The Understanding of the Brain,* 178–181.

8. T. V. A. Bliss and T. Lomo, *Journal of Physiology* (1970): 207–220.

9. Eccles, *The Understanding of the Brain*, 183.

10. Thatcher and John, *Functional Neuroscience*, 258.

11. W. J. Freeman, *Mass Action in the Nervous System* (New York: Academic Press, 1975).

12. Karl Pribram, *Languages of the Brain* (Englewood Cliffs, N.J.: Prentice Hall, 1971), 150–157.

13. Penfield, *The Mystery of the Mind*, 27.

14. Ibid., 31–33.

15. Thatcher and John, *Functional Neuroscience*, 218.

16. Larry R. Squire, "Mechanisms of Memory," *Science* 232 (June 27, 1986): 1612–1619.

17. R. W. Sperry, "Hemisphere Deconnection and Unity in Conscious Awareness," *American Psychologist,* 23 (October 1968): 723–733.

18. Sperry, "Some Effects of Disconnecting the Cerebral Hemispheres," 217 no. 4566 *Science* (September 24, 1982): 1223–1226.

Chapter 11: The Brain and the Electronic Computer

1. Wooldridge, *The Machinery of the Brain*.

Chapter 12: Free Will

1. D. J. O'Connor, *Free Will* (Garden City, N.Y.: Doubleday & Co., 1971), 121.

2. J. L. Austin, "Ifs and Cans," in *Free Will and Determinism,* edited by Bernard Berofsky (New York: Harper and Row, 1966), 295–322.

3. P. H. Nowell Smith in ibid., 322–339.

4. Roderick M. Chisholm, in ibid., 339–345.

5. Wooldridge, *The Mechanical Man: The Physical Basis of Intelligent Life* (New York: McGraw-Hill, 1968).

6. Gilbert Ryle, *The Concept of Mind* (New York: Barnes & Noble, 1949), 63.

7. Ibid., 64.

8. Jerome A. Shaffer, *Philosophy of Mind* (Englewood Cliffs, N.J.: Prentice-Hall, 1968), 110.

9. William Earle, *Objectivity: An Essay in Phenomenological*

Ontology (Chicago: Quadrangle Paperbacks, Quadrangle Books, 1958), 49.

Chapter 13: The Seat of Consciousness

1. Charles Symonds, "Reflections," in *The Mystery of the Mind*, Wilder Penfield, ed., 96–97.
2. Ibid., 97.
3. Wooldridge, *The Machinery of the Brain*, 138.
4. Penfield, *The Mystery of the Mind*, 15.
5. Thatcher and John, *Functional Neuroscience*, 88.
6. Penfield, *The Mystery of the Mind*, 18.
7. Ibid., 37–42.
8. Ibid., 39.
9. Sperry, *Some Effects of Disconnecting the Cerebral Hemispheres*, 1226.

Chapter 14: Brain-Mind Concepts

1. Thatcher and John, *Functional Neuroscience*, 305–306.
2. Ibid., 306.
3. Ibid.
4. Wooldridge, *The Machinery of the Brain*, 238.
5. Symonds, "Reflections," in Penfield, *The Mystery of the Mind*, 91.
6. Wooldridge, *The Machinery of the Brain*, 240.
7. Ibid., 220.
8. Penfield, *The Mystery of the Mind*, 63–64.
9. Ibid., 75–76.
10. Sperry, "Bridging Science and Values: A Unifying View of Mind and Brain," in *Mind and the Brain: The Many Faceted Problems*, ed. Eccles (New York: Paragon House, 1982), 259–260.
11. Eccles, "Evolution of the Conscious Self," in *The Human Mind*, ed. John D. Roslansky (Amsterdam: North Holland Publishing Co., 1969), 24.
12. Eccles, *The Understanding of the Brain*, 227.
13. Karl R. Popper and John C. Eccles, *The Self and Its Brain* (New York: Springer-Verlag, 1981), 356.
14. Ibid., 362.
15. Ibid., 355.

16. Ibid., 369–370.
17. Ibid., 366.
18. Ibid., 559–560.
19. Ibid., 554.
20. Bohm, *Wholeness and the Implicate Order.*
21. Ibid., 211.
22. Ibid., 151.
23. Ibid., 155.
24. Ibid., 210.
25. Ibid., 209.

Chapter 16: Critique of the Mechanistic Theories of Mind

1. Thatcher and John, *Foundational Neuroscience,* 90, 91.
2. Shaffer, *Philosophy of Mind,* 76.

Chapter 17: Energy of Mind

1. Penfield, *The Mystery of the Mind,* 48.
2. Ibid., 56.
3. Wilhelm Ostwald, "Lectures on Natural Philosophy." See Heisenberg, *The Physicist's Conception of Nature,* 149–150.
4. Capra, *The Tao of Physics,* 5.
5. Andrzej Tautman, "Conservation Laws in General Relativity," in *Gravitation: An Introduction to Current Research,* ed. Louis Witten (New York: John Wiley and Sons, 1962), 169.
6. Hermann Weyl, *Philosophy of Mathematics and Natural Science,* trans. Olaf Helmer (Princeton: Princeton University Press, 1949), 182–183.
7. Eccles, "Evolution of the Conscious Self," in *The Human Mind,* 25.
8. Benjamin Pinkel, *The Existential Adventure: The Roles of Science and Belief* (Marina del Rey, Calif.: DeVorss and Co., 1976), 57.

Chapter 19: The Laws Relating to Energy of Mind

1. R. L. Gregory, *Eye and Brain* (London: Weidenfeld and Nicolson, 1969), 86.

2. Stanley A. Gelfand, *Hearing: An Introduction to Psychological and Physiological Acoustics*, 226–235.

3. Eccles, *The Understanding of the Brain* 11, figs. 1–7.

4. Granit, *Receptors and Sensory Perception*, 8–13.

5. Sigmund Freud, *A General Introduction to Psychoanalysis* (New York: Washington Square Press, 1960).

6. Edmund Husserl, *Cartesian Meditations: An Introduction to Phenomenology* (The Hague: Martinus Nijhoff, 1977), 17.

7. Ibid., 21.

8. Ibid., 41.

9. Ibid., 42.

10. Ibid., 44.

11. Sperry, "Some Effects of Disconnecting the Cerebral Hemispheres," 1226.

12. Charles Sherrington, *Man on His Nature* (New York: Macmillan Co., 1941), 351.

13. René Descartes, *Meditations on First Philosophy*, trans. Laurence J. Lafleur (Indianapolis: Bobbs-Merrill Co., 1977), 15.

Chapter 20: Some Philosophical Considerations

1. Shaffer, *Philosophy of Mind*.

2. George Berkeley, *The Principles of Human Knowledge* (LaSalle, Ill.: The Open Court Publishing Co., 1957), 32.

3. J. J. C. Smart, "Sensations and Brain Processes," in *The Philosophy of Mind*, ed. V. C. Chapell (Englewood Cliffs: Prentice-Hall, 1981), 162.

4. Jerry A. Fodor, "The Mind Body Problem," 244, no. 1, *Scientific American* (January 1981): 114.

5. Ibid., 122.

6. P. F. Strawson, "Persons," in *The Philosophy of Mind*, 135.

7. Josiah Royce, *The World and the Individual*, 2d series (New York: Macmillan Co., 1929), 240.

8. Thatcher and John, *Functional Neuroscience*, 305.

Chapter 22: The Human Psyche

1. From the Dead Sea Scrolls. Taken from Eccles "Evolution and the Conscious Self," in *The Human Mind*, 27.

Index